COLLECT BRITISH STAMPS

A STANLEY GIBBONS CHECKLIST OF

THE STAMPS OF GREAT BRITAIN

1994 (Forty-sixth) Edition

STANLEY GIBBONS LTD

By Appointment to H. M. the Queen
Stanley Gibbons Ltd, London Philatelists.

London and Ringwood

COLLECT BRITISH STAMPS

The 1994 Edition

From the famous Penny Black of 1840 to the absorbing issues of today, the stamps of Great Britain are highly popular with collectors. *Collect British Stamps* has been our message since very early days – but particularly since the First Edition of this checklist in September 1967. This 46th edition includes all the recent issues. Prices have been carefully revised to reflect today's market. Total sales of *Collect British Stamps* are now over 3½ million copies.

Collect British Stamps appears in the autumn of each year. A more detailed Great Britain catalogue, the *Concise*, is published each spring. The *Great Britain Concise* incorporates many additional listings covering watermark varieties, phosphor omitted errors, missing colour errors, stamp booklets and special commemorative First Day Cover postmarks. It is ideally suited for the collector who wishes to discover more about GB stamps.

Listings in this edition of *Collect British Stamps* include all 1994 issues which have appeared up to the publication date.

Scope. *Collect British Stamps* comprises:
- All stamps with different watermark (*wmk*) or perforation (*perf*).
- Visible plate numbers on the Victorian issues.
- Graphite-lined and phosphor issues, including variations in the number of phosphor bands.
- First Day Covers for Definitives from 1952, Regionals and all Special Issues.
- Presentation, Gift and Souvenir Packs.
- Post Office Yearbooks.
- Regional issues and War Occupation stamps of Guernsey and Jersey.
- Postage Due and Official Stamps.
- Post Office Picture Cards (PHQ cards).
- Commemorative gutter pairs and "Traffic Light" gutter pairs listed as mint sets.
- Royal Mail Postage Labels priced as sets and on P.O. First Day Cover.

Stamps of the independent postal administrations of Guernsey, Isle of Man and Jersey are contained in *Collect Channel Islands and Isle of Man Stamps*.

Layout. Stamps are set out chronologically by date of issue. In the catalogue lists the first numeral is the Stanley Gibbons catalogue number; the black (boldface) numeral alongside is the type number referring to the respective illustration. A blank in this column implies that the number immediately above is repeated. The denomination and colour of the stamp are then shown. Before February 1971 British currency was:

$£1 = 20s$ One pound=twenty shillings *and*
$1s = 12d$ One shilling=twelve pence.

Upon decimalisation this became:

$£1 = 100p$ One pound=one hundred (new) pence.

The catalogue list then shows two price columns. The left-hand is for unused stamps and the right-hand for used. Corresponding small boxes are provided in which collectors may wish to check off the items in their collection.

Our method of indicating prices is:
Numerals for pence, e.g. 10 denotes 10p (10 pence). Numerals for pounds and pence, e.g. 4·25 denotes £4·25 (4 pounds and 25 pence).
For £100 and above, prices are in whole pounds and so include the £ sign and omit the zeros for pence.

Colour illustrations. The colour illustrations of stamps are intended as a guide only; they may differ in shade from the originals.

Size of illustrations. To comply with Post Office regulations stamp illustrations are three-quarters linear size. Separate illustrations of surcharges, overprints and watermarks are actual size.

Prices. Prices quoted in this catalogue are our selling prices at the time the book went to press. They are for stamps in fine condition; in issues where condition varies we may ask more for the superb and less for the sub-standard. The unused prices for stamps of Queen Victoria to King Edward VIII are for lightly hinged examples. Unused prices for King George VI and Queen Elizabeth II are for unmounted mint (though when not available unmounted, mounted stamps are often supplied at a lower price). Prices for used stamps refer to postally used copies. All prices are subject to change without prior notice and we give no guarantee to supply all stamps priced, since it is not possible to keep every catalogued item in stock. Individual low value stamps sold at 399, Strand are liable to an additional handling charge.

In the price columns:

† = Does not exist.

(—) or blank = Exists, or may exist, but price cannot be quoted.

* = Not normally issued (the so-called 'Abnormals' of 1862–80).

Perforations. The 'perforation' is the number of holes in a length of 2 cm, as measured by the Gibbons *Instanta* gauge. The stamp is viewed against a dark background with the transparent gauge put on top of it. Perforations are quoted to the nearest half. Stamps without perforation are termed 'imperforate'.

From 1992 certain stamps occur with a large elliptical (oval) hole inserted in each line of vertical perforations. The £10 definitive, No. 1658, is unique in having two such holes in the horizontal perforations.

Elliptical perforations

Se-tenant combinations. *Se-tenant* means 'joined together'. Some sets include stamps of different design arranged *se-tenant* as blocks or strips and these are often collected unsevered as issued. Where such combinations exist the stamps are priced both mint and used, as singles or complete combinations. The set price for mint refers to the unsevered combination plus singles of any other values in the set. The used set price is for single stamps of all values.

First day covers. Prices for first day covers are for complete sets used on plain covers (1924, 1925, 1929) or on special covers (1935 onwards), the stamps of which are cancelled with ordinary operational postmarks (1924–1962) or by the *standard* "First Day of Issue" postmarks (1963 onwards). The British Post Office did not provide "First Day" treatment for every definitive issued after 1963. Where the stamps in a set were issued on different days, prices are for a cover from each day.

Presentation Packs. Special packs comprising slip-in cards with printed information inside a protective covering, were introduced for the 1964 Shakespeare issue. Collectors packs, containing commemoratives from the preceding twelve months, were issued from 1967. Some packs with text in German from 1968–69 exist as does a Japanese version of the pack for Nos. 916/17. Yearbooks, hardbound and illustrated in colour within a slip cover, joined the product range in 1984.

PHQ cards. Since 1973 the Post Office has produced a series of picture cards, which can be sent through the post as postcards. Each card shows an enlarged colour reproduction of a current British stamp, either of one or more values from a set or of all values. Cards are priced here in fine mint condition for sets complete as issued. The Post Office gives each card a 'PHQ' serial number, hence the term. The cards are usually on sale shortly before the date of issue of the stamps, but there is no officially designated 'first day'.

Used prices are for cards franked with the stamp depicted, on the obverse or reverse; the stamp being cancelled with an official postmark for first day of issue.

Gutter pairs. All modern Great Britain commemoratives are produced in sheets containing two panes of stamps separated by a blank horizontal or vertical margin known as a gutter. This feature first made its appearance on some supplies of the 1972 Royal Silver Wedding 3p, and marked the introduction of Harrison & Sons' new "Jumelle" stamp-printing press. There are advantages for both the printer and the Post Office in such a layout which has now been used for all commemorative issues since 1974.

The term "gutter pair" is used for a pair of stamps separated by part of the blank gutter margin.

Traffic light gutter pair

Gutter pair

Most printers include some form of colour check device on the sheet margins, in addition to the cylinder or plate numbers. Harrison & Sons use round "dabs", or spots of colour, resembling traffic lights. For the period from the 1972 Royal Silver Wedding until the end of 1979 these colour dabs appeared in the gutter margin. Gutter pairs showing these "traffic lights" are worth considerably more than the normal version.

Catalogue numbers used. The checklist uses the same catalogue numbers as the Stanley Gibbons *British Commonwealth* Catalogue (Part 1), 1994 edition.

Latest issue date for stamps recorded in this edition is 1 November 1994.

STANLEY GIBBONS LTD

Head Office: 399 Strand, London WC2R 0LX. Auction Room and Specialist Stamp Departments—Open Monday-Friday 9.30 a.m. to 5 p.m.

Shop—Open Monday to Friday 8.30 a.m. to 6 p.m. and Saturday 10.00 a.m. to 4 p.m.

Telephone 071-836 8444 for all departments

Stanley Gibbons Publications:
Editorial, Sales Offices and
 Distribution Centre,
5, Parkside, Christchurch Road,
Ringwood, Hants BH24 3SH.
Telephone 0425 472363

ISBN: 0-85259-384-8
© Stanley Gibbons Ltd 1994

2 Embossed Issues

Prices are for stamps cut square and with average to fine embossing. Stamps with exceptionally clear embossing are worth more.

10

11

12

13

1847–54 *Wmk* **13** (6d), *no wmk* (*others*)   *Imperforate*

59	**10**	6d lilac	..	..	£2500	£400	☐ ☐
57	**11**	10d brown	..	..	£2250	£575	☐ ☐
54	**12**	1s green	..	..	£2750	£350	☐ ☐

3 Surface-printed Issues

IDENTIFICATION. Check first whether the design includes corner letters or not, as mentioned for 'Line-engraved Issues'. The checklist is divided up according to whether any letters are small or large, also whether they are white (uncoloured) or printed in the colour of the stamp. Further identification then depends on watermark.

PERFORATION. Except for Nos. 126/9 all the following issues of Queen Victoria are perf 14.

14

15 Small Garter   **16 Medium Garter**   **17 Large Garter**

18

19

20 Emblems

No corner letters

1855–57 (*i*) *Wmk Small Garter Type* **15**

62	**14**	4d red	..	..	..	£2250	£170	☐ ☐

(*ii*) *Wmk Medium Garter Type* **16**

64	**14**	4d red	..	..	..	£1800	£150	☐ ☐

(*iii*) *Wmk Large Garter Type* **17**

66a	**14**	4d red	..	..	..	£600	40·00	☐ ☐

(*iv*) *Wmk Emblems Type* **20**

70	**18**	6d lilac	..	..	..	£500	40·00	☐ ☐
72	**19**	1s green	..	..	..	£650	£140	☐ ☐

Plate numbers. Stamps Nos. 90/163 should be checked for the 'plate numbers' indicated, as this affects valuation (the cheapest plates are priced here). The mark '*Pl.*' shows that several numbers exist, priced in a separate list overleaf.

Plate numbers are the small numerals appearing in duplicate in some part of the frame design or adjacent to the lower corner letters (in the 5s value a single numeral above the lower inscription).

21

22

23

24

25

Small white corner letters

1862–64 *Wmk Emblems Type* **20**, *except* 4d (*Large Garter Type* **17**)

77	**21**	3d red	..	..	..	£700	£100	☐ ☐
80	**22**	4d red	..	..	..	£500	35·00	☐ ☐
84	**23**	6d lilac	..	..	..	£650	30·00	☐ ☐
87	**24**	9d bistre	..	..	..	£1100	£130	☐ ☐
90	**25**	1s green *Pl.*	..	..	..	£700	65·00	☐ ☐

26   **27**   **28** (hyphen in SIX-PENCE)   **32**   **33** Spray of Rose   **34**

29   **30**   **31**

Large white corner letters

1865–67 Wmk Emblems Type **20**, except 4d (Large Garter Type **17**)

Cat.	Type			Un.	Used		
92	26	3d red (Plate 4)	..	£375	40·00	☐	☐
94	27	4d vermilion Pl.		£225	15·00	☐	☐
97	28	6d lilac Pl.	.. ..	£350	28·00	☐	☐
98	29	9d straw Pl.		£700	£200	☐	☐
99	30	10d brown (Plate 1)	†	£12000			☐
101	31	1s green (Plate 4)		£650	65·00	☐	☐

1867–80 Wmk Spray of Rose Type **33**

				Un.	Used		
103	26	3d red Pl.	... ...	£200	12·00	☐	☐
105	28	6d lilac (with hyphen) (Plate 6)		£550	30·00	☐	☐
109		6d mauve (without hyphen) Pl.		£275	25·00	☐	☐
111	29	9d straw (Plate 4)		£600	£100	☐	☐
112	30	10d brown Pl.		£1000	£150	☐	☐
117	31	1s green Pl.	... ...	£350	10·00	☐	☐
119	32	2s blue Pl.	... ...	£950	60·00	☐	☐
121		2s brown (Plate 1)		£6000	£1000	☐	☐

1872–73 Wmk Spray of Rose Type **33**

				Un.	Used		
123	34	6d brown Pl.	...	£350	18·00	☐	☐
125		6d grey (Plate 12)		£600	90·00	☐	☐

PLATE NUMBERS
on stamps
of 1862–83

Cat. No.		Plate No.	Un.	Used		

Small White Corner Letters (1862–64)

| 90 | 1s green | 2 | £700 | 65·00 | ☐ | ☐ |
| | | 3 | £11000 | | ☐ | ☐ |

Plate 2 is actually numbered as '1' and Plate 3 as '2' on the stamps.

Large White Corner Letters (1865–83)

103	3d red	4	£300	50·00	☐	☐
		5	£200	14·00	☐	☐
		6	£225	12·00	☐	☐
		7	£275	15·00	☐	☐
		8	£250	14·00	☐	☐
		9	£250	20·00	☐	☐
		10	£275	42·00	☐	☐
94	4d verm	7	£300	19·00	☐	☐
		8	£250	19·00	☐	☐
		9	£250	15·00	☐	☐
		10	£300	30·00	☐	☐
		11	£250	15·00	☐	☐
		12	£225	15·00	☐	☐
		13	£250	17·00	☐	☐
		14	£300	35·00	☐	☐
97	6d lilac	5	£350	28·00	☐	☐
		6	£1000	55·00	☐	☐
109	6d mauve	9	£275	25·00	☐	☐
		10	£12000			☐
123	6d brown	11	£350	18·00	☐	☐
		12	£750	55·00	☐	☐

98	9d straw	4	£700	£200	☐	☐
		5	£10000	*	☐	☐
112	10d brown	1	£1000	£150	☐	☐
		2	£12000	£2500	☐	☐
117	1s green	4	£350	15·00	☐	☐
		5	£400	12·00	☐	☐
		6	£550	10·00	☐	☐
		7	£550	30·00	☐	☐
119	2s blue	1	£950	60·00	☐	☐
		3	*	£3000	☐	☐
126	5s red	1	£2500	£275	☐	☐
		2	£3500	£350	☐	☐

Large Coloured Corner Letters (1873–83)

139	2½d mauve	1	£225	25·00	☐	☐
		2	£225	25·00	☐	☐
		3	£400	30·00	☐	☐
141	2½d mauve	3	£500	30·00	☐	☐
		4	£225	14·00	☐	☐
		5	£225	18·00	☐	☐
		6	£225	14·00	☐	☐
		7	£225	14·00	☐	☐
		8	£225	18·00	☐	☐
		9	£225	14·00	☐	☐
		10	£250	20·00	☐	☐
		11	£225	14·00	☐	☐
		12	£225	18·00	☐	☐
		13	£225	18·00	☐	☐
		14	£225	14·00	☐	☐
		15	£225	14·00	☐	☐
		16	£225	14·00	☐	☐
		17	£550	90·00	☐	☐
142	2½d blue	17	£180	20·00	☐	☐
		18	£200	12·00	☐	☐
		19	£180	10·00	☐	☐
		20	£180	10·00	☐	☐

157	2½d blue	21	£225	9·00	☐	☐
		22	£180	8·00	☐	☐
		23	£180	8·00	☐	☐
143	3d red	11	£200	12·00	☐	☐
		12	£225	14·00	☐	☐
		14	£250	15·00	☐	☐
		15	£200	14·00	☐	☐
		16	£200	14·00	☐	☐
		17	£225	14·00	☐	☐
		18	£225	14·00	☐	☐
		19	£200	14·00	☐	☐
		20	£200	30·00	☐	☐
158	3d red	20	£250	45·00	☐	☐
		21	£200	30·00	☐	☐
152	4d verm	15	£600	£140	☐	☐
		16	*	£10000	☐	☐
153	4d green	15	£450	95·00	☐	☐
		16	£400	90·00	☐	☐
		17	*	£6000	☐	☐
160	4d brown	17	£180	25·00	☐	☐
		18	£180	25·00	☐	☐
147	6d grey	13	£225	22·00	☐	☐
		14	£225	22·00	☐	☐
		15	£225	20·00	☐	☐
		16	£225	20·00	☐	☐
		17	£300	38·00	☐	☐
161	6d grey	17	£180	25·00	☐	☐
		18	£150	25·00	☐	☐
150	1s green	8	£325	35·00	☐	☐
		9	£325	35·00	☐	☐
		10	£300	35·00	☐	☐
		11	£300	35·00	☐	☐
		12	£250	28·00	☐	☐
		13	£250	28·00	☐	☐
		14	*	£10000	☐	☐
163	1s brown	13	£275	45·00	☐	☐
		14	£225	45·00	☐	☐

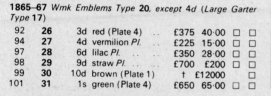

35

36

37

38

39 Maltese Cross   40 Large Anchor

1867–83 (*i*) *Wmk Maltese Cross Type* **39**   Perf 15½×15

126	**35**	5s red *Pl.*	£2500	£275	☐ ☐
128	**36**	10s grey (Plate 1)	£18000	£850	☐ ☐
129	**37**	£1 brown (Plate 1)	£22000	£1200	☐ ☐

(*ii*) *Wmk Large Anchor Type* **40**   Perf 14

134	**35**	5s red (Plate 4)	£4500	£850	☐ ☐
131	**36**	10s grey (Plate 1)	£20000	£1200	☐ ☐
132	**37**	£1 brown (Plate 1)	£28000	£2250	☐ ☐
137	**38**	£5 orange (Plate 1)	£4250	£1200	☐ ☐

41

42

43

44

45

46

47 Small Anchor

48 Orb

Large coloured corner letters

1873–80 (*i*) *Wmk Small Anchor Type* **47**

139	**41**	2½d mauve *Pl.*	£225	25·00	☐ ☐

(*ii*) *Wmk Orb Type* **48**

141	**41**	2½d mauve *Pl.*	£225	14·00	☐ ☐
142		2½d blue *Pl.*	£180	10·00	☐ ☐

(*iii*) *Wmk Spray of Rose Type* **33**

143	**42**	3d red *Pl.*	£200	12·00	☐ ☐
145	**43**	6d pale buff (Plate 13)	*	£4500	☐ ☐
147		6d grey *Pl.*	£225	20·00	☐ ☐
150	**44**	1s green *Pl.*	£250	28·00	☐ ☐
151		1s brown (Plate 13)	£1100	£190	☐ ☐

(*iv*) *Wmk Large Garter Type* **17**

152	**45**	4d vermilion *Pl.*	£600	£140	☐ ☐
153		4d green *Pl.*	£400	90·00	☐ ☐
154		4d brown (Plate 17)	£600	£150	☐ ☐
156	**46**	8d orange (Plate 1)	£550	£110	☐ ☐

49 Imperial Crown   (**50**) Surcharges in red   (**51**)

1880–83 *Wmk Imperial Crown Type* **49**

157	**41**	2½d blue *Pl.*	£180	8·00	☐ ☐
158	**42**	3d red *Pl.*	£200	30·00	☐ ☐
159		3d on 3d lilac (surch Type **50**)	£225	70·00	☐ ☐
160	**45**	4d brown *Pl.*	£180	25·00	☐ ☐
161	**43**	6d grey *Pl.*	£150	25·00	☐ ☐
162		6d on 6d lilac (surch Type **51**)	£200	70·00	☐ ☐
163	**44**	1s brown *Pl.*	£225	45·00	☐ ☐

52

53

54

55

56

1880–81 Wmk Imperial Crown Type 49

164	**52**	½d green	..	..	15·00	3·00	□	□
166	**53**	1d brown	..	..	5·00	2·00	□	□
167	**54**	1½d brown	..	..	80·00	14·00	□	□
168	**55**	2d red ..	..		95·00	30·00	□	□
169	**56**	5d indigo	..	..	£350	45·00	□	□

57

Die I

Die II

1881 Wmk Imperial Crown Type 49
(a) 14 dots in each corner, Die I

171	**57**	1d lilac	..		75·00	12·00	□	□

(b) 16 dots in each corner, Die II

| 173 | **57** | 1d lilac | .. | .. | 1·00 | 30 | □ | □ |

58

59

60

Coloured letters in the corners

1883-84 Wmk Anchor Type **40**

179	**58**	2s 6d deep lilac	..	..	£200	65·00	□	□
181	**59**	5s red		..	£400	80·00	□	□
183	**60**	10s blue..		..	£750	£250	□	□

61

1884 Wmk 3 Imperial Crowns Type **49**

185	**61**	£1 brown	..	..£10000	£850	□	□

1888 Wmk 3 Orbs Type **48**

186	**61**	£1 brown	..	..£16000	£1300	□	□

1891 Wmk 3 Imperial Crowns Type **49**

212	**61**	£1 green	..	..£2000	£350	□	□

62   63   64

65   66

1883–84 Wmk Imperial Crown Type 49 (sideways on horiz. designs)

187	52	½d blue	..	..	8·00	1·50	□	□
188	62	1½d lilac	..	..	55·00	18·00	□	□
189	63	2d lilac	..	..	70·00	30·00	□	□
190	64	2½d lilac	..	..	40·00	5·00	□	□
191	65	3d lilac	..	..	90·00	40·00	□	□
192	66	4d dull green	..		£225	95·00	□	□
193	62	5d dull green	..		£225	95·00	□	□
194	63	6d dull green	..		£250	£100	□	□
195	64	9d dull green	..		£475	£225	□	□
196	65	1s dull green	..		£350	£130	□	□

The above prices are for stamps in the true dull green colour. Stamps which have been soaked, causing the colour to run, are virtually worthless.

67   **68**   **69**

KING EDWARD VII
1901 (22 Jan.)–1910 (6 May)

70   **71**   **72**

79   **80**   **81**

73   **74**   **75**

82   **83**   **84**

76   **77**   **78**

85   **86**   **87**

'Jubilee' issue
1887–1900 *The bicoloured stamps have the value tablets, or the frames including the value tablets, in the second colour.*
Wmk Imperial Crown Type **49**

197	**67**	½d	vermilion	..	1·00	50	☐ ☐
213		½d	green*	.. ..	1·00	60	☐ ☐
198	**68**	1½d	purple and green		10·00	4·00	☐ ☐
200	**69**	2d	green and red	..	15·00	6·00	☐ ☐
201	**70**	2½d	purple on blue		10·00	75	☐ ☐
203	**71**	3d	purple on yellow		15·00	1·50	☐ ☐
205a	**72**	4d	green and brown		18·00	7·25	☐ ☐
206	**73**	4½d	green and red	..	5·00	20·00	☐ ☐
207a	**74**	5d	purple and blue		18·00	6·00	☐ ☐
208	**75**	6d	purple on red		18·00	7·50	☐ ☐
209	**76**	9d	purple and blue		40·00	25·00	☐ ☐
210	**77**	10d	purple and red		35·00	22·00	☐ ☐
211	**78**	1s	green	.. ..	£130	30·00	☐ ☐
214		1s	green and red	..	45·00	80·00	☐ ☐
	Set of 14		.. .. ..		£325	£190	☐ ☐

*The ½d. No. 213. in blue is a colour changeling.

88   **89**

90   **91**   **92**

93

7

1902–13 *Wmks Imperial Crown Type* **49** ($\frac{1}{2}$d to 1s); *Anchor Type* **40** (2s 6d to 10s); *Three Crowns Type* **49** (£1)

(*a*) *Perf* 14

215	79	$\frac{1}{2}$d	blue-green	..	50	30	☐ ☐
217		$\frac{1}{2}$d	yellow-green	..	40	30	☐ ☐
219		1d	red	..	40	30	☐ ☐
222	80	1$\frac{1}{2}$d	purple and green		10·00	4·75	☐ ☐
291	81	2d	green and red ..		10·00	5·00	☐ ☐
231	82	2$\frac{1}{2}$d	blue	..	4·00	2·50	☐ ☐
232	83	3d	purple on yellow		15·00	2·50	☐ ☐
236a	84	4d	green and brown		15·00	7·00	☐ ☐
240		4d	orange	..	7·50	6·50	☐ ☐
294	85	5d	purple and blue		10·00	4·75	☐ ☐
245	79	6d	purple	..	12·00	4·00	☐ ☐
249	86	7d	grey	.. ..	3·00	6·00	☐ ☐
307	87	9d	purple and blue		30·00	22·00	☐ ☐
311	88	10d	purple and red ..		30·00	20·00	☐ ☐
314	89	1s	green and red ..		25·00	8·00	☐ ☐
260	90	2s 6d	lilac	..	£100	45·00	☐ ☐
263	91	5s	red ..	..	£100	55·00	☐ ☐
319	92	10s	blue	..	£300	£200	☐ ☐
320	93	£1	green	..	£750	£300	☐ ☐
	Set of 15 (*to* 1s)			..	£160	90·00	☐ ☐

(*b*) *Perf* 15×14

279a	79	$\frac{1}{2}$d	green	..	20·00	20·00	☐ ☐
282		1d	red ..	..	8·00	3·00	☐ ☐
283	82	2$\frac{1}{2}$d	blue	..	10·00	5·00	☐ ☐
285	83	3d	purple on yellow		15·00	4·00	☐ ☐
286	84	4d	orange	..	10·00	6·00	☐ ☐
	Set of 5		.. ..	..	55·00	40·00	☐ ☐

KING GEORGE V
1910 (6 May)–1936 (20 Jan.)

PERFORATION. All the following issues are Perf 15×14 except vertical commemorative stamps which are 14×15, unless otherwise stated.

94 (Hair dark)　　　95 (Lion unshaded)　　96

1911–12 *Wmk Imperial Crown Type* **49**

322	94	$\frac{1}{2}$d	green	.. ..	2·50	1·00	☐ ☐
327	95	1d	red ..	.. ..	2·25	1·00	☐ ☐

1912 *Wmk Royal Cypher* (*'Simple'*) *Type* **96**

335	94	$\frac{1}{2}$d	green	.. ..	20·00	22·00	☐ ☐
336	95	1d	red ..	.. ..	12·00	12·00	☐ ☐

97 (Hair light)　　　98 (Lion shaded)　　99

1912 *Wmk Imperial Crown Type* **49**

339	97	$\frac{1}{2}$d	green	.. ..	3·00	50	☐ ☐
341	98	1d	red	..	1·25	50	☐ ☐

1912 *Wmk Royal Cypher* (*'Simple'*) *Type* **96**

344	97	$\frac{1}{2}$d	green	.. ..	2·50	70	☐ ☐
345	98	1d	red ..	..	4·00	50	☐ ☐

1912 *Wmk Royal Cypher* (*'Multiple'*) *Type* **99**

348	-	97	$\frac{1}{2}$d	green	.. ..	6·00	4·00	☐ ☐
350		98	1d	red ..	..	5·00	4·50	☐ ☐

100　　　　　101　　　　　102

103　　　　　104

1912–24 *Wmk Royal Cypher Type* **96**

351	101	$\frac{1}{2}$d	green	.. ..	30	25	☐ ☐
357	100	1d	red ..	..	30	25	☐ ☐
362	101	1$\frac{1}{2}$d	brown	.. ..	1·00	25	☐ ☐
368	102	2d	orange	..	1·00	50	☐ ☐
372	100	2$\frac{1}{2}$d	blue	.. ..	4·50	1·00	☐ ☐
375	102	3d	violet	..	2·00	75	☐ ☐
379		4d	grey-green	..	4·00	75	☐ ☐
381	103	5d	brown	..	3·50	3·00	☐ ☐
385		6d	purple	..	6·00	1·50	☐ ☐
		a. Perf 14			60·00	85·00	☐ ☐
387		7d	olive-green	..	6·00	3·75	☐ ☐
390		8d	black on yellow		15·00	6·50	☐ ☐
392	104	9d	black	..	5·00	2·50	☐ ☐
393a		9d	olive-green	..	65·00	15·00	☐ ☐
394		10d	blue	..	9·00	12·00	☐ ☐
395		1s	brown	.. ..	15·00	1·00	☐ ☐
	Set of 15		.. ..	..	£130	45·00	☐ ☐

1913 *Wmk Royal Cypher ('Multiple') Type* **99**

397	**101**	½d green	..	..	50·00	95·00	☐ ☐
398	**100**	1d red ..	..	..	£110	£130	☐ ☐

See also Nos. 418/29.

105

106

T 105. Background around portrait consists of horizontal lines

1913–18 *Wmk Single Cypher Type* **106**   *Perf* 11 × 12

413a	**105**	2s 6d brown	..	..	55·00	25·00	☐ ☐
416		5s red	..	..	£125	45·00	☐ ☐
417		10s blue	..	..	£200	80·00	☐ ☐
403		£1 green	..	..	£950	£600	☐ ☐
		Set of 4	..	..	£1200	£700	☐ ☐

See also Nos. 450/2.

107

1924–26 *Wmk Block Cypher Type* **107**

418	**101**	½d green	..	..	15	25	☐ ☐
419	**100**	1d red ..	..	..	15	25	☐ ☐
420	**101**	1½d brown	..	..	15	25	☐ ☐
421	**102**	2d orange	..	..	75	80	☐ ☐
422	**100**	2½d blue	..	..	3·00	1·25	☐ ☐
423	**102**	3d violet	..	..	4·00	1·00	☐ ☐
424		4d grey-green	..	..	6·00	1·00	☐ ☐
425	**103**	5d brown	..	..	10·00	1·60	☐ ☐
426a		6d purple	..	..	1·50	50	☐ ☐
427	**104**	9d olive-green	..	..	5·00	2·25	☐ ☐
428		10d blue	..	..	15·00	16·00	☐ ☐
429		1s brown	..	..	10·00	1·00	☐ ☐
		Set of 12	..	..	50·00	23·00	☐ ☐

For full information on all future British issues, collectors should write to the British Post Office Philatelic Bureau, 20 Brandon Street, Edinburgh EH3 5TT

108

109

British Empire Exhibition

1924–25 *Wmk* **107**   *Perf* 14

		(*a*) 23.4.24.	*Dated* '1924'					
430	**108**	1d red ..	..	..	5·00	6·00	☐ ☐
431	**109**	1½d brown	..	..	7·50	11·00	☐ ☐
		First Day Cover	..	..		£350	☐
		(*b*) 9.5.25.	*Dated* '1925'					
432	**108**	1d red ..	..	..	8·00	17·00	☐ ☐
433	**109**	1½d brown	..	..	25·00	50·00	☐ ☐
		First Day Cover	..	..		£1200	☐

110   111   112

113 St George and the Dragon

114

9

Ninth Universal Postal Union Congress
1929 (10 MAY) (a) Wmk **107**

434	110	½d green	..	..	1·50	1·50	□ □
435	111	1d red ..	..	..	1·50	1·50	□ □
436		1½d brown			1·00	1·00	□ □
437	112	2½d blue	..	..	7·50	9·00	□ □
		(b) Wmk **114** Perf 12					
438	113	£1 black	..		£550	£400	□ □
434/7		Set of 4	..	..	10·00	11·50	□ □
434/7		First Day Cover (4 vals.)				£500	□
434/8		First Day Cover (5 vals.)		..		£2500	□

120

121

122

123

115

116

117

118

119

Silver Jubilee
1935 (7 MAY) Wmk **107**

453	120	½d green	..	..	25	20	□ □
454	121	1d red	..	..	1·00	1·00	□ □
455	122	1½d brown	..	..	25	20	□ □
456	123	2½d blue	..	..	4·00	5·50	□ □
		Set of 4	..	..	5·00	6·00	□ □
		First Day Cover	..	..		£400	□

1934–36 Wmk **107**

439	115	½d green	..	..	10	25	□ □
440	116	1d red ..	..	..	10	25	□ □
441	115	1½d brown	..	..	10	25	□ □
442	117	2d orange	..	..	25	25	□ □
443	116	2½d blue	..	..	75	60	□ □
444	117	3d violet	..	..	75	50	□ □
445		4d grey-green	..	..	1·00	55	□ □
446	118	5d brown	..	..	4·00	1·50	□ □
447	119	9d olive-green	..	..	10·00	1·60	□ □
448		10d blue	..	..	12·00	8·00	□ □
449		1s brown	..	..	12·00	50	□ □
		Set of 11	..	..	35·00	11·00	□ □

KING EDWARD VIII
1936 (20 Jan.–10 Dec.)

124

125

T 105 (re-engraved). Background around portrait consists of horizontal and diagonal lines
1934 Wmk **106** Perf 11 × 12

450	105	2s 6d brown	..	..	40·00	15·00	□ □
451		5s red ..	..	..	90·00	50·00	□ □
452		10s blue	..	..	£225	50·00	□ □
		Set of 3	..	..	£300	£100	□ □

1936 Wmk **125**

457	124	½d green	..	..	20	15	□ □
458		1d red ..	..	..	50	20	□ □
459		1½d brown	..	..	25	15	□ □
460		2½d blue	..	..	25	60	□ □
		Set of 4	..	..	1·00	1·00	□ □

KING GEORGE VI
1936 (11 Dec.)–1952 (6 Feb.)

126 King George VI
and Queen Elizabeth

127

131 King George VI

131a

132

132a

Coronation

1937 (13 MAY) *Wmk* **127**

461	126	1½d brown	..	..	40	25	□ □
		First Day Cover	..	..		24·00	□

128

129

130

King George VI and National Emblems

133

1939–48 *Wmk* **133** *Perf* 14

476	131	2s 6d brown	..	..	40·00	7·00	□ □
476*a*		2s 6d green	..	..	9·00	1·00	□ □
477	131a	5s red	..	..	18·00	1·50	□ □
478	132	10s dark blue	..	..	£130	18·00	□ □
478*a*		10s bright blue	..	..	40·00	4·50	□ □
478*b*	132a	£1 brown	..	..	15·00	19·00	□ □
		Set of 6	..	..	£225	45·00	□ □

1937–47 *Wmk* **127**

462	128	½d green	..	..	10	15	□ □
463		1d scarlet	..	..	10	15	□ □
464		1½d brown	..	..	20	15	□ □
465		2d orange	..	..	1·25	45	□ □
466		2½d blue	..	..	25	15	□ □
467		3d violet	..	..	4·00	60	□ □
468	129	4d green	..	..	35	40	□ □
469		5d brown	..	..	2·75	35	□ □
470		6d purple	..	..	1·50	40	□ □
471	130	7d green	..	..	3·75	50	□ □
472		8d red	..	..	4·50	50	□ □
473		9d deep green	..	..	6·00	50	□ □
474		10d blue	..	..	5·50	60	□ □
474*a*		11d plum	..	..	2·50	1·50	□ □
475		1s brown	..	..	7·00	40	□ □
		Set of 15	..	..	35·00	6·00	□ □

For later printings of the lower values in apparently lighter
shades and different colours, see Nos. 485/90 and 503/8.

For full information on all future British issues, collectors
should write to the British Post Office Philatelic Bureau, 20
Brandon Street, Edinburgh EH3 5TT

134 Queen Victoria and King George VI

Centenary of First Adhesive Postage Stamps

1940 (6 MAY) *Wmk* **127** *Perf* 14½ × 14

479	134	½d green	..	..	30	20	□ □
480		1d red	..	..	90	40	□ □
481		1½d brown	..	..	30	30	□ □
482		2d orange	..	..	50	40	□ □
483		2½d blue	..	..	1·90	80	□ □
484		3d violet	..	..	4·00	3·50	□ □
		Set of 6	..	..	7·00	5·00	□ □
		First Day Cover	..		35·00		□

Head as Nos. 462/7, but lighter background

1941–42 Wmk **127**

485	**128**	½d pale green	..	15	10	☐ ☐
486		1d pale red	..	15	10	☐ ☐
487		1½d pale brown	..	75	45	☐ ☐
488		2d pale orange	..	50	40	☐ ☐
489		2½d light blue	..	15	10	☐ ☐
490		3d pale violet	..	1·50	50	☐ ☐
	Set of 6	.. .. ..		2·75	1·50	☐ ☐

135 Symbols of Peace and Reconstruction

136 Symbols of Peace and Reconstruction

Victory

1946 (11 JUNE) Wmk **127**

491	**135**	2½d blue	.. ..	25	15	☐ ☐
492	**136**	3d violet	.. ..	25	15	☐ ☐
	First Day Cover	.. .. ..		42·00		☐

137 King George VI and Queen Elizabeth

138 King George VI and Queen Elizabeth

Royal Silver Wedding

1948 (26 APR.) Wmk **127**

493	**137**	2½d blue	..	30	30	☐ ☐
494	**138**	£1 blue	..	32·00	32·00	☐ ☐
	First Day Cover	.. .. ..		£375		☐

1948 (10 MAY)

Stamps of 1d and 2½d showing seaweed-gathering were on sale at eight Head Post Offices elsewhere in Great Britain, but were primarily for use in the Channel Islands and are listed there (see after Regional Issues).

139 Globe and Laurel Wreath

140 'Speed'

141 Olympic Symbol

142 Winged Victory

Olympic Games

1948 (29 JULY) Wmk **127**

495	**139**	2½d blue	.. ..	10	10	☐ ☐
496	**140**	3d violet	.. ..	30	30	☐ ☐
497	**141**	6d purple	.. ..	60	30	☐ ☐
498	**142**	1s brown	.. ..	1·25	1·50	☐ ☐
	Set of 4	.. ..		2·00	2·00	☐ ☐
	First Day Cover	.. ..		28·00		☐

143 Two Hemispheres

144 U.P.U. Monument, Berne

145 Goddess Concordia, Globe and Points of Compass

146 Posthorn and Globe

75th Anniversary of Universal Postal Union

1949 (10 OCT.) Wmk **127**

499	**143**	2½d blue	..	10	10	☐ ☐
500	**144**	3d violet	..	30	40	☐ ☐
501	**145**	6d purple	..	60	75	☐ ☐
502	**146**	1s brown	..	1·25	1·50	☐ ☐
	Set of 4	.. .. ..		2·00	2·75	☐ ☐
	First Day Cover			50·00		☐ ☐

4d as No. 468 and others as Nos. 485/9, but colours changed

1950–51 *Wmk* **127**

503	**128**	½d	pale orange	..	10	15	☐	☐
504		1d	light blue		15	15	☐	☐
505		1½d	pale green	..	25	30	☐	☐
506		2d	pale brown	..	25	20	☐	☐
507		2½d	pale red ..	..	20	15	☐	☐
508	**129**	4d	light blue	..	1·50	1·10	☐	☐
	Set of 6		.. .. ..		2·25	1·75	☐	☐

147 HMS *Victory*

148 White Cliffs of Dover

149 St George and the Dragon

150 Royal Coat of Arms

1951 (3 MAY) *Wmk* **133** *Perf* 11 × 12

509	**147**	2s 6d green	..	..	8·00	75	☐	☐
510	**148**	5s red ..		..	30·00	1·50	☐	☐
511	**149**	10s blue	..	..	18·00	10·00	☐	☐
512	**150**	£1 brown	..	..	40·00	14·00	☐	☐
	Set of 4				85·00	22·00	☐	☐

151 Commerce and Prosperity

152 Festival Symbol

Festival of Britain

1951 (3 MAY) *Wmk* **127**

513	**151**	2½d red ..	..	..	· 25	15	☐	☐
514	**152**	4d blue	..	..	50	45	☐	☐
	First Day Cover ..	.. ..			16·00			☐

QUEEN ELIZABETH II
6 February, 1952

153 Tudor Crown

154

155

156

157

158

159

160

1952–54 *Wmk* **153**

515	**154**	½d	orange	.. ..	10	15	☐	☐
516		1d	blue	.. ..	20	20	☐	☐
517		1½d	green	.. ..	10	15	☐	☐
518		2d	brown	.. ..	20	15	☐	☐
519	**155**	2½d	red ..	..	10	15	☐	☐
520		3d	lilac	..	1·00	30	☐	☐
521	**156**	4d	blue	..	3·00	80	☐	☐
		4½d	(*See Nos.* 577, 594 609 *and* 616b)					
522	**157**	5d	brown	..	90	2·00	☐	☐
523		6d	purple	..	3·00	60	☐	☐
524		7d	green	..	9·00	3·50	☐	☐
525	**158**	8d	magenta	..	1·00	60	☐	☐
526		9d	bronze-green	..	22·00	3·00	☐	☐
527		10d	blue	..	18·00	3·00	☐	☐
528		11d	plum	..	30·00	16·00	☐	☐
529	**159**	1s	bistre	..	1·00	40	☐	☐
530	**160**	1s 3d	green	..	4·50	2·00	☐	☐
531	**159**	1s 6d	indigo	..	11·00	2·75	☐	☐
	Set of 17		.. ..		95·00	28·00	☐	☐

First Day Covers

5 Dec. 1952	Nos. 517, 519	.. .. ..	6·00	☐
6 July 1953	Nos. 522, 525, 529	.. ..	25·00	☐
31 Aug. 1953	Nos. 515/16, 518 ..	.. ..	20·00	☐
2 Nov. 1953	Nos. 521, 530/1	.. ..	50·00	☐
18 Jan. 1954	Nos. 520, 523/4	.. ..	30·00	☐
8 Feb. 1954	Nos. 526/8	.. .. ..	60·00	☐

See also Nos. 540/56, 561/6, 570/94 and 599/618a.

161

162

163

164

Coronation

1953 (3 June) *Wmk* **153**

532	**161**	2½d	red	10	25	☐	☐
533	**162**	4d	blue	40	1·50	☐	☐
534	**163**	1s 3d	green	3·50	2·50	☐	☐
535	**164**	1s 6d	blue	7·00	3·50	☐	☐
	Set of 4		.. ..	10·00	7·00	☐	☐
	First Day Cover		.. .. ..		40·00		☐

165 St Edward's Crown

166 Carrickfergus Castle

167 Caernarvon Castle

168 Edinburgh Castle

169 Windsor Castle

1955 (1–23 Sept.) *Wmk* **165** *Perf* 11 × 12

536	**166**	2s 6d	brown	10·00	2·00	☐	☐
537	**167**	5s	red	35·00	3·50	☐	☐
538	**168**	10s	blue	85·00	11·00	☐	☐
539	**169**	£1	black	£1·50	28·00	☐	☐
	Set of 4		.. ..	£250	40·00	☐	☐
	First Day Cover (*Nos.* 538/9) (1 Sept.)		.. ..		£400		☐
	First Day Cover (*Nos.* 536/7) (23 Sept.)		.. ..		£175		☐

See also Nos 595*a*/8*a* and 759/62.

1955–58 *Wmk* **165**

540	**154**	½d	orange	10	15	☐	☐
541		1d	blue	25	15	☐	☐
542		1½d	green	10	15	☐	☐
543		2d	red-brown ..	20	20	☐	☐
543*b*		2d	light red-brown	20	15	☐	☐
544	**155**	2½d	red	20	15	☐	☐
545		3d	lilac	20	15	☐	☐
546	**156**	4d	blue	1·40	40	☐	☐
547	**157**	5d	brown	5·50	3·50	☐	☐
548*a*		6d	purple	3·50	80	☐	☐
549		7d	green	50·00	7·50	☐	☐
550	**158**	8d	magenta	6·00	1·00	☐	☐
551		9d	bronze-green ..	23·00	2·25	☐	☐
552		10d	blue	19·00	2·25	☐	☐
553		11d	plum	40	1·50	☐	☐
554	**159**	1s	bistre	19·00	40	☐	☐
555	**160**	1s 3d	green	27·00	1·50	☐	☐
556	**159**	1s 6d	indigo	19·00	1·25	☐	☐
	Set of 18		.. ..	£150	22·00	☐	☐

170 Scout Badge and 'Rolling Hitch'

171 'Scouts coming to Britain'

172 Globe within a Compass

173

World Scout Jubilee Jamboree

1957 (1 Aug.) *Wmk* **165**

557	**170**	2½d	red	15	10	☐	☐
558	**171**	4d	blue	50	1·00	☐	☐
559	**172**	1s 3d	green	5·00	4·50	☐	☐
	Set of 3		.. ..	5·00	4·50	☐	☐
	First Day Cover		.. .. ..		12·00		☐

46th Inter Parliamentary Union Conference

1957 (12 Sept.) *Wmk* **165**

560	**173**	4d	blue	1·00	1·00	☐	☐
	First Day Cover		.. .. ..		90·00		☐

Graphite-lined and Phosphor Issues

These are used in connection with automatic sorting machinery, originally experimentally at Southampton but now also operating elsewhere. In such areas these stamps were the normal issue, but from mid 1967 *all* low-value stamps bear phosphor markings.

The graphite lines were printed in black on the back, beneath the gum; two lines per stamp except for the 2d (*see below*).

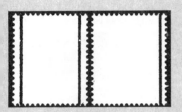

174   **175** (2d only)
(Stamps viewed from back)

In November 1959, phosphor bands, printed on the front, replaced the graphite. They are wider than the graphite, not easy to see, but show as broad vertical bands at certain angles to the light.

Values representing the rate for printed papers (and second class mail from 1968) have one band and others have two, three or four bands according to size and format. From 1972 onwards some commemorative stamps were printed with 'all-over' phosphor.

In the small stamps the bands are on each side with the single band at left (except where otherwise stated). In the large-size commemorative stamps the single band may be at left, centre or right varying in different issues. The bands are vertical on both horizontal and vertical designs except where otherwise stated.

See also notes on page 35.

Graphite-lined issue

1957 (19 Nov.) *Two graphite lines on the back, except 2d value, which has one line. Wmk* **165**

561	**154**	½d orange	..	..	20	30	☐	☐
562		1d blue	..	..	20	35	☐	☐
563		1½d green	..	..	30	1·25	☐	☐
564		2d light red-brown			2·50	1·50	☐	☐
565	**155**	2½d red ..	..	..	7·00	6·25	☐	☐
566		3d lilac	..	..	30	50	☐	☐
	Set of 6	..	..	..	9·50	9·00	☐	☐
	First Day Cover	..	..		60·00		☐	

See also Nos. 587/94.

176 Welsh Dragon

177 Flag and Games Emblem

178 Welsh Dragon

Sixth British Empire and Commonwealth Games, Cardiff

1958 (18 July) *Wmk* **165**

567	**176**	3d lilac	..	..	15	10	☐	☐
568	**177**	6d mauve	..	..	25	45	☐	☐
569	**178**	1s 3d green	..	..	2·25	2·25	☐	☐
	Set of 3	..	..	..	2·25	2·25	☐	☐
	First Day Cover	..	..	..	55·00		☐	

179 Multiple Crowns

WATERMARK. All the following issues to No. 755 are Watermark **179** (sideways on the vertical commemorative stamps) unless otherwise stated.

1958–65 *Wmk* **179**

570	**154**	½d orange	..	..	10	10	☐	☐
571		1d blue	..	..	10	10	☐	☐
572		1½d green	..	..	10	15	☐	☐
573		2d light red-brown			10	10	☐	☐
574	**155**	2½d red ..		..	10	10	☐	☐
575		3d lilac	..	..	10	10	☐	☐
576a	**156**	4d blue	..	..	15	10	☐	☐
577		4½d brown	..	..	10	15	☐	☐
578	**157**	5d brown	..	..	25	20	☐	☐
579		6d purple	..	..	25	15	☐	☐
580		7d green	..	..	40	20	☐	☐
581	**158**	8d magenta ..		..	40	15	☐	☐
582		9d bronze-green	..		40	15	☐	☐
583		10d blue	..	..	1·00	15	☐	☐
584	**159**	1s bistre	..	..	40	15	☐	☐
585	**160**	1s 3d green	..	..	25	15	☐	☐
586	**159**	1s 6d indigo	..	..	5·00	40	☐	☐
	Set of 17	..	..	..	8·00	2·10	☐	☐
	First Day Cover (*No.* 577) (9 Feb. 1959)	..	..		45·00		☐	

For full information on all future British issues, collectors should write to the British Post Office Philatelic Bureau, 20 Brandon Street, Edinburgh EH3 5TT

Graphite-lined issue

1958–59 Two graphite lines on the back, except 2d value, which has one line. Wmk **179**

587	154	½d orange	1·25	2·25	☐ ☐
588		1d blue	1·00	1·50	☐ ☐
589		1½d green	40·00	40·00	☐ ☐
590		2d light red-brown	6·00	3·25	☐ ☐
591	155	2½d red	8·00	10·00	☐ ☐
592		3d lilac	50	50	☐ ☐
593	156	4d blue	3·50	4·50	☐ ☐
594		4½d brown	5·00	4·50	☐ ☐
		Set of 8	60·00	60·00	☐ ☐

The prices quoted for Nos. 587 and 589 are for examples with inverted watermark. Stamps with upright watermark are priced at: ½d £6 mint or used and 1½d £95 mint, £60 used.

1959–63 Wmk **179**   Perf 11 × 12

595a	166	2s 6d brown ., ..	50	30	☐ ☐
596a	167	5s red	1·00	60	☐ ☐
597a	168	10s blue	2·50	3·00	☐ ☐
598a	169	£1 black	10·00	5·00	☐ ☐
		Set of 4	13·00	8·00	☐ ☐

Phosphor-Graphite issue

1959 (18 Nov.) Two phosphor bands on front and two graphite lines on back, except 2d value, which has one band on front and one line on back

(a) Wmk **165**

599	154	½d orange	4·00	6·00	☐ ☐
600		1d blue	8·00	6·00	☐ ☐
601		1½d green	2·00	5·00	☐ ☐

(b) Wmk **179**

605	154	2d light red-brown (1 band)	4·50	3·75	☐ ☐
606	155	2½d red	20·00	11·00	☐ ☐
607		3d lilac	9·00	8·00	☐ ☐
608	156	4d blue	12·00	25·00	☐ ☐
609		4½d brown	35·00	15·00	☐ ☐
		Set of 8	80·00	70·00	☐ ☐

Phosphor issue

1960–67 Two phosphor bands on front, except where otherwise stated. Wmk **179**

610	154	½d orange	10	15	☐ ☐
611		1d blue	10	10	☐ ☐
612		1½d green	10	20	☐ ☐
613		2d light red-brown (1 band)	18·00	20·00	☐ ☐
613a		2d light red-brown (2 bands) ..	10	10	☐ ☐
614	155	2½d red (2 bands) ..	10	40	☐ ☐
614a		2½d red (1 band) ..	40	75	☐ ☐
615		3d lilac (2 bands) ..	60	45	☐ ☐
615c		3d lilac (1 side band)	35	60	☐ ☐
615e		3d lilac (1 centre band)	25	40	☐ ☐

616a	156	4d blue	15	15	☐ ☐
616b		4½d brown	15	25	☐ ☐
616c	157	5d brown	20	25	☐ ☐
617		6d purple	40	20	☐ ☐
617a		7d green	60	25	☐ ☐
617b	158	8d magenta	20	25	☐ ☐
617c		9d bronze-green ..	60	25	☐ ☐
617d		10d blue	80	35	☐ ☐
617e	159	1s bistre	40	20	☐ ☐
618	160	1s 3d green	1·75	2·50	☐ ☐
618a	159	1s 6d indigo	2·00	1·00	☐ ☐
		Set of 17 (one of each value)	7·00	6·00	☐ ☐

No. 615c exists with the phosphor band at the left or right of the stamp.

180 Postboy of 1660   **181** Posthorn of 1660

Tercentenary of Establishment of 'General Letter Office'

1960 (7 July)

619	180	3d lilac	20	10	☐ ☐
620	181	1s 3d green	3·50	3·50	☐ ☐
		Set of 2	3·50	3·50	☐ ☐
		First Day Cover		40·00	☐

182 Conference Emblem

First Anniversary of European Postal and Telecommunications Conference

1960 (19 Sept.)

621	182	6d green and purple	40	60	☐ ☐
622		1s 6d brown and blue	5·25	4·50	☐ ☐
		Set of 2	5·25	4·50	☐ ☐
		First Day Cover		28·00	☐

183 Thrift Plant   **184** 'Growth of Savings'

185 Thrift Plant

Centenary of Post Office Savings Bank

1961 (28 Aug.)

623	**183**	2½d black and red ..	10	10	☐	☐
624	**184**	3d orange-brown and violet ..	10	10	☐	☐
625	**185**	1s 6d red and blue	2·25	2·00	☐	☐
	Set of 3		2·25	2·00	☐	☐
	First Day Cover			60·00	☐	

186 C.E.P.T. Emblem

187 Doves and Emblem

188 Doves and Emblem

European Postal and Telecommunications (C.E.P.T.) Conference, Torquay

1961 (18 Sept.)

626	**186**	2d orange, pink and brown ..	10	10	☐	☐
627	**187**	4d buff, mauve and ultramarine ..	20	10	☐	☐
628	**188**	10d turquoise, green and blue ..	40	35	☐	☐
	Set of 3		60	50	☐	☐
	First Day Cover			2·50	☐	

189 Hammer Beam Roof, Westminster Hall

190 Palace of Westminster

Seventh Commonwealth Parliamentary Conference

1961 (25 Sept.)

629	**189**	6d purple and gold	25	25	☐	☐
630	**190**	1s 3d green and blue	2·50	2·00	☐	☐
	Set of 2		2·50	2·00	☐	☐
	First Day Cover			26·00	☐	

191 'Units of Productivity'

192 'National Productivity'

193 'Unified Productivity'

National Productivity Year

1962 (14 Nov.) *Wmk* **179** (*inverted on 2½d and 3d*)

631	**191**	2½d green and red ..	20	10	☐	☐
		p. Phosphor ..	1·00	40	☐	☐
632	**192**	3d blue and violet	25	10	☐	☐
		p. Phosphor ..	1·00	50	☐	☐
633	**193**	1s 3d red, blue and green ..	1·75	1·60	☐	☐
		p. Phosphor ..	25·00	18·00	☐	☐
	Set of 3 (Ordinary) ..		2·00	1·60	☐	☐
	Set of 3 (Phosphor) ..		25·00	18·00	☐	☐
	First Day Cover (Ordinary) ..			30·00	☐	
	First Day Cover (Phosphor)			95·00	☐	

194 Campaign Emblem and Family   **195** Children of Three Races

Freedom from Hunger

1963 (21 Mar.) *Wmk* **179** (*inverted*)

634	**194**	2½d crimson and pink	10	10	☐	☐
		p. Phosphor ..	1·00	1·00	☐	☐
635	**195**	1s 3d brown and yellow	2·00	1·75	☐	☐
		p. Phosphor ..	25·00	18·00	☐	☐
	Set of 2 (Ordinary)		2·00	1·75	☐	☐
	Set of 2 (Phosphor) ..		25·00	18·00	☐	☐
	First Day Cover (Ordinary) ..			28·00	☐	
	First Day Cover (Phosphor) ..			30·00	☐	

196 'Paris Conference'

Paris Postal Conference Centenary

1963 (7 MAY) *Wmk* **179** (*inverted*)

636	**196**	6d green and mauve	50	40	☐	☐
		p. *Phosphor* ..	6·00	5·00	☐	☐
		First Day Cover (Ordinary) ..		12·00	☐	
		First Day Cover (Phosphor) ..		20·00	☐	

197 Posy of Flowers

198 Woodland Life

National Nature Week

1963 (16 MAY)

637	**197**	3d multicoloured ..	25	20	☐	☐
		p. *Phosphor* ..	50	50	☐	☐
638	**198**	4½d multicoloured ..	40	40	☐	☐
		p. *Phosphor* ..	2·50	2·50	☐	☐
		Set of 2 (Ordinary)	60	60	☐	☐
		Set of 2 (Phosphor) ..	3·00	3·00	☐	☐
		First Day Cover (Ordinary) ..		· 14·00	☐	
		First Day Cover (Phosphor)		28·00	☐	

199 Rescue at Sea

200 19th-century Lifeboat

201 Lifeboatmen

Ninth International Lifeboat Conference, Edinburgh

1963 (31 MAY)

639	**199**	2½d blue, black and red	10	10	☐	☐
		p. *Phosphor*	40	50	☐	☐
640	**200**	4d multicoloured ..	40	30	☐	☐
		p. *Phosphor*	20	50	☐	☐
641	**201**	1s 6d sepia, yellow and blue ..	2·50	2·50	☐	·☐
		p. *Phosphor* ..	32·00	24·00	☐	☐
		Set of 3 (Ordinary) ..	2·75	2·50	☐	☐
		Set of 3 (Phosphor) ..	32·00	24·00	☐	☐
		First Day Cover (Ordinary)		26·00		☐
		First Day Cover (Phosphor)		38·00		☐

202 Red Cross   203

204   205 'Commonwealth Cable'

Red Cross Centenary Congress

1963 (15 AUG.)

642	**202**	3d red and lilac ..	10	10	☐	☐
		p. *Phosphor* ..	60	60	☐	☐
643	**203**	1s 3d red, blue and grey	2·75	2·50	☐	☐
		p. *Phosphor* ..	40·00	30·00	☐	☐
644	**204**	1s 6d red, blue and bistre ..	2·50	2·50	☐	☐
		p. *Phosphor* ..	30·00	20·00	☐	☐
		Set of 3 (Ordinary) ..	5·00	4·50	☐	☐
		Set of 3 (Phosphor) ..	65·00	45·00	☐	☐
		First Day Cover (Ordinary) ..		28·00		☐
		First Day Cover (Phosphor)		60·00		☐

Opening of COMPAC (Trans-Pacific Telephone Cable)

1963 (3 DEC.)

645	**205**	1s 6d blue and black	2·50	2·25	☐	☐
		p. *Phosphor*	15·00	13·50	☐	☐
		First Day Cover (Ordinary) ..		22·00		☐
		First Day Cover (Phosphor)		24·00		☐

206 Puck and Bottom
(*A Midsummer Night's Dream*)

207 Feste (*Twelfth Night*)

213 Beddgelert Forest Park, Snowdonia ('Forestry')

214 Nuclear Reactor, Dounreay ('Technological Development')

208 Balcony Scene
(*Romeo and Juliet*)

209 Eve of Agincourt
(*Henry V*)

20th International Geographical Congress, London

1964 (1 JULY)

651	211	2½d multicoloured		10	10	☐	☐
		p. Phosphor		50	40	☐	☐
652	212	4d multicoloured		25	25	☐	☐
		p. Phosphor		75	70	☐	☐
653	213	8d multicoloured		60	50	☐	☐
		p. Phosphor		1·75	1·50	☐	☐
654	214	1s 6d multicoloured		3·25	3·25	☐	☐
		p. Phosphor		21·00	18·00	☐	☐
		Set of 4 (Ordinary)		4·00	4·00	☐	☐
		Set of 4 (Phosphor)		21·00	18·00	☐	☐
		First Day Cover (Ordinary)			18·00		☐
		First Day Cover (Phosphor)			27·00		☐
		Presentation Pack (Ordinary)		85·00		☐	

210 Hamlet contemplating Yorick's skull (*Hamlet*) and Queen Elizabeth II

Shakespeare Festival

1964 (23 APR.)   *Perf* 11×12 (2s 6d) *or* 15×14 (*others*)

646	206	3d bis, blk & vio-bl		10	10	☐	☐
		p. Phosphor		20	30	☐	☐
647	207	6d multicoloured		20	30	☐	☐
		p. Phosphor		60	70	☐	☐
648	208	1s 3d multicoloured		90	1·00	☐	☐
		p. Phosphor		5·75	5·50	☐	☐
649	209	1s 6d multicoloured		1·25	1·00	☐	☐
		p. Phosphor		9·00	5·75	☐	☐
650	210	2s 6d deep slate-purple		2·00	2·00	☐	☐
		Set of 5 (Ordinary)		4·00	4·00	☐	☐
		Set of 4 (Phosphor)		13·00	11·00	☐	☐
		First Day Cover (Ordinary)			11·00		☐
		First Day Cover (Phosphor)			11·00		☐
		Presentation Pack (Ordinary)	10·00			☐	

215 Spring Gentian

216 Dog Rose

PRESENTATION PACKS were first introduced by the G.P.O. for the Shakespeare Festival issue. The packs include one set of stamps and details of the designs, the designer and the stamp printer. They were issued for almost all later definitive and special issues.

217 Honeysuckle

218 Fringed Water Lily

Tenth International Botanical Congress, Edinburgh

1964 (5 AUG.)

655	215	3d vio. blue & green		10	10	☐	☐
		p. Phosphor		20	20	☐	☐
656	216	6d multicoloured		20	20	☐	☐
		p. Phosphor		1·50	1·00	☐	☐
657	217	9d multicoloured		1·60	2·00	☐	☐
		p. Phosphor		4·50	3·00	☐	☐
658	218	1s 3d multicoloured		2·50	1·90	☐	☐
		p. Phosphor		20·00	16·00	☐	☐
		Set of 4 (Ordinary)		4·00	4·00	☐	☐
		Set of 4 (Phosphor)		24·00	18·00	☐	☐
		First Day Cover (Ordinary)			18·00		☐
		First Day Cover (Phosphor)			28·00		☐
		Presentation Pack (Ordinary)	85·00			☐	

211 Flats near Richmond Park
('Urban Development')

212 Shipbuilding Yards, Belfast
('Industrial Activity')

219 Forth Road Bridge

220 Forth Road and Railway Bridges

Opening of Forth Road Bridge

1964 (4 SEPT.)

659	**219**	3d	black, blue and violet	15	10	☐	☐
		p.	Phosphor	50	50	☐	☐
660	**220**	6d	black, blue and red	45	40	☐	☐
		p.	Phosphor	4·50	4·50	☐	☐
		Set of 2 (Ordinary)		60	50	☐	☐
		Set of 2 (Phosphor)		5·00	5·00	☐	☐
		First Day Cover (Ordinary)			5·00	☐	
		First Day Cover (Phosphor)			10·00	☐	
		Presentation Pack (Ordinary)		£200		☐	

221 Sir Winston Churchill

222 Sir Winston Churchill

Churchill Commemoration

1965 (8 JULY)

661	**221**	4d	black and drab	15	10	☐	☐
		p.	Phosphor	30	30	☐	☐
662	**222**	1s 3d	black and grey	45	30	☐	☐
		p.	Phosphor	3·00	3·25	☐	☐
		Set of 2 (Ordinary)		60	40	☐	☐
		Set of 2 (Phosphor)		3·00	3·25	☐	☐
		First Day Cover (Ordinary)			2·00	☐	
		First Day Cover (Phosphor)			4·50	☐	
		Presentation Pack (Ordinary)		13·00		☐	

223 Simon de Montfort's Seal

224 Parliament Buildings
(after engraving by Hollar, 1647)

700th Anniversary of Simon de Montfort's Parliament

1965 (19 JULY)

663	**223**	6d	green	10	10	☐	☐
		p.	Phosphor	40	40	☐	☐
664	**224**	2s 6d	black, grey and drab	1·25	1·25	☐	☐
		Set of 2 (Ordinary)		1·25	1·25	☐	☐
		First Day Cover (Ordinary)			12·00	☐	
		First Day Cover (Phosphor)			16·00	☐	
		Presentation Pack (Ordinary)		35·00		☐	

225 Bandsmen and Banner

226 Three Salvationists

Salvation Army Centenary

1965 (9 AUG.)

665	**225**	3d	multicoloured	10	10	☐	☐
		p.	Phosphor	40	40	☐	☐
666	**226**	1s 6d	multicoloured	1·00	1·00	☐	☐
		p.	Phosphor	2·75	3·25	☐	☐
		Set of 2 (Ordinary)		1·10	1·10	☐	☐
		Set of 2 (Phosphor)		3·00	3·50	☐	☐
		First Day Cover (Ordinary)			20·00	☐	
		First Day Cover (Phosphor)			22·00	☐	

227 Lister's Carbolic Spray

228 Lister and Chemical Symbols

Centenary of Joseph Lister's Discovery of Antiseptic Surgery

1965 (1 SEPT.)

667	**227**	4d	indigo, chestnut and grey	10	10	☐	☐
		p.	Phosphor	15	20	☐	☐
668	**228**	1s	black, purple and blue	1·00	1·25	☐	☐
		p.	Phosphor	2·40	2·40	☐	☐
		Set of 2 (Ordinary)		1·10	1·25	☐	☐
		Set of 2 (Phosphor)		2·50	2·50	☐	☐
		First Day Cover (Ordinary)			9·50	☐	
		First Day Cover (Phosphor)			8·50	☐	

229 Trinidad Carnival Dancers   **230** Canadian Folk-dancers

Commonwealth Arts Festival

1965 (1 SEPT.)

669	**229**	6d	black and orange	10	10	☐	☐
		p.	Phosphor	30	30	☐	☐
670	**230**	1s 6d	black and violet	1·25	1·50	☐	☐
		p.	Phosphor	2·25	2·25	☐	☐
		Set of 2 (Ordinary)		1·25	1·50	☐	☐
		Set of 2 (Phosphor)		2·50	2·50	☐	☐
		First Day Cover (Ordinary)			10·00		☐
		First Day Cover (Phosphor)			10·00		☐

231 Flight of Spitfires   **232** Pilot in Hurricane

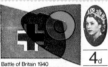

233 Wing-tips of Spitfire and Messerschmitt 'ME-109'   **234** Spitfires attacking Heinkel 'HE-111' Bomber

235 Spitfire attacking Stuka Dive-bomber   **236** Hurricanes over Wreck of Dornier 'DO-17z2' Bomber

The above were issued together *se-tenant* in blocks of six (3 × 2) within the sheet.

237 Anti-aircraft Artillery in Action   **238** Air-battle over St Paul's Cathedral

25th Anniversary of Battle of Britain

1965 (13 SEPT.)

671	**231**	4d	olive and black	30	35	☐	☐
	a.	Block of 6					
		Nos. 671/6		5·50	5·50	☐	☐
	p.	Phosphor		40	50	☐	☐
	pa.	Block of 6					
		Nos. 671p/6p		10·50	9·00	☐	☐
672	**232**	4d	olive, blackish olive and black	30	35	☐	☐
		p.	Phosphor	40	50	☐	☐
673	**233**	4d	multicoloured	30	35	☐	☐
		p.	Phosphor	40	50	☐	☐
674	**234**	4d	olive and black	30	35	☐	☐
		p.	Phosphor	40	50	☐	☐
675	**235**	4d	olive and black	30	35	☐	☐
		p.	Phosphor	40	50	☐	☐
676	**236**	4d	multicoloured	30	35	☐	☐
		p.	Phosphor	40	50	☐	☐
677	**237**	9d	violet, orange and purple	1·25	1·25	☐	☐
		p.	Phosphor	1·25	80	☐	☐
678	**238**	1s 3d	multicoloured	1·25	1·25	☐	☐
		p.	Phosphor	1·25	80	☐	☐
		Set of 8 (Ordinary)		6·50	4·25	☐	☐
		Set of 8 (Phosphor)		12·00	4·25	☐	☐
		First Day Cover (Ordinary)			18·00		☐
		First Day Cover (Phosphor)			18·00		☐
		Presentation Pack (Ordinary)		48·00			☐

239 Tower and Georgian Buildings   **240** Tower and 'Nash' Terrace, Regent's Park

Opening of Post Office Tower

1965 (8 OCT.)

679	**239**	3d	yellow, blue and green	10	10	☐	☐
		p.	Phosphor	10	10	☐	☐
680	**240**	1s 3d	green and blue	65	75	☐	☐
		p.	Phosphor	50	50	☐	☐
		Set of 2 (Ordinary)		75	85	☐	☐
		Set of 2 (Phosphor)		60	60	☐	☐
		First Day Cover (Ordinary)			6·00		☐
		First Day Cover (Phosphor)			8·00		☐
		Presentation Pack (Ordinary)		3·00			☐
		Presentation Pack (Phosphor)		3·00			☐

241 U.N. Emblem   **242** I.C.Y. Emblem

20th Anniversary of UNO and International Co-operation Year

1965 (25 Oct.)

681	**241**	3d blk, orge & bl ..	15	20	☐	☐
		p. Phosphor ..	25	25	☐	☐
682	**242**	1s 6d blk, pur & bl	1·10	90	☐	☐
		p. Phosphor	2·75	2·50	☐	☐
	Set of 2 (Ordinary)		1·25	1·10	☐	☐
	Set of 2 (Phosphor)		2·75	2·75	☐	☐
	First Day Cover (Ordinary) ..			9·00		☐
	First Day Cover (Phosphor)			9·50		☐

243 Telecommunications Network   **244** Radio Waves and Switchboard

I.T.U. Centenary

1965 (15 Nov.)

683	**243**	9d multicoloured ..	20	20	☐	☐
		p. Phosphor	60	50	☐	☐
684	**244**	1s 6d multicoloured ..	1·40	1·10	☐	☐
		p. Phosphor ..	4·50	4·50	☐	☐
	Set of 2 (Ordinary)		1·50	1·25	☐	☐
	Set of 2 (Phosphor) ..		5·00	5·00	☐	☐
	First Day Cover (Ordinary) ..			11·00		☐
	First Day Cover (Phosphor)			11·50		☐

245 Robert Burns (after Skirving chalk drawing)   **246** Robert Burns (after Nasmyth portrait)

Burns Commemoration

1966 (25 Jan.)

685	**245**	4d blk, indigo & bl ..	15	15	☐	☐
		p. Phosphor	25	25	☐	☐
686	**246**	1s 3d blk, bl & orge ..	70	70	☐	☐
		p. Phosphor	1·00	1·00	☐	☐
	Set of 2 (Ordinary) ..		85	85	☐	☐
	Set of 2 (Phosphor)		1·25	1·25	☐	☐
	First Day Cover (Ordinary) ..			2·50		☐
	First Day Cover (Phosphor)			3·50		☐
	Presentation Pack (Ordinary)			35·00		☐

247 Westminster Abbey   **248** Fan Vaulting, Henry VII Chapel

900th Anniversary of Westminster Abbey

1966 (28 Feb.)   Perf 15×14 (3d) or 11×12 (2s 6d)

687	**247**	3d black, brown and blue	15	10	☐	☐
		p. Phosphor ..	30	30	☐	☐
688	**248**	2s 6d black	85	90	☐	☐
	Set of 2		1·00	1·00	☐	☐
	First Day Cover (Ordinary) ..			4·50		☐
	First Day Cover (Phosphor)			9·50		☐
	Presentation Pack (Ordinary)		17·00		☐

249 View near Hassocks, Sussex   **250** Antrim, Northern Ireland

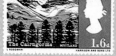

251 Harlech Castle, Wales   **252** Cairngorm Mountains, Scotland

Landscapes

1966 (2 May)

689	**249**	4d black, yellow-green and blue	15	15	☐	☐
		p. Phosphor	15	15	☐	☐
690	**250**	6d black, green and blue	15	15	☐	☐
		p. Phosphor ..	25	25	☐	☐
691	**251**	1s 3d black, yellow and blue	35	35	☐	☐
		p. Phosphor ..	35	35	☐	☐
692	**252**	1s 6d black, orange and blue	50	50	☐	☐
		p. Phosphor ..	50	50	☐	☐
	Set of 4 (Ordinary)		1·00	1·00	☐	☐
	Set of 4 (Phosphor)		1·00	1·00	☐	☐
	First Day Cover (Ordinary)			6·00		☐
	First Day Cover (Phosphor)			6·00		☐

253 Players with Ball **260** Cup Winners

254 Goalmouth Mêlée **255** Goalkeeper saving Goal

World Cup Football Competition

1966 (1 June)

693	**253**	4d multicoloured ..	15	10	☐	☐
		p. Phosphor	15	10	☐	☐
694	**254**	6d multicoloured ..	20	20	☐	☐
		p. Phosphor	20	20	☐	☐
695	**255**	1s 3d multicoloured ..	50	50	☐	☐
		p. Phosphor	50	50	☐	☐
		Set of 3 (Ordinary) ..	75	75	☐	☐
		Set of 3 (Phosphor) ..	75	75	☐	☐
		First Day Cover (Ordinary) ..		6·50		☐
		First Day Cover (Phosphor)		6·50		☐
		Presentation Pack (Ordinary)	14·00			☐

256 Black-headed Gull **257** Blue Tit

258 Robin **259** Blackbird

The above were issued *se-tenant* in blocks of four within the sheet.

British Birds

1966 (8 Aug.)

696	**256**	4d multicoloured ..	10	15	☐	☐
		a. Block of 4				
		Nos. 696/9 ..	1·00	1·00	☐	☐
		p. Phosphor	10	15	☐	☐
		pa. Block of 4				
		Nos. 696p/9p ..	1·00	1·00	☐	☐
697	**257**	4d multicoloured ..	10	15	☐	☐
		p. Phosphor	10	15	☐	☐
698	**258**	4d multicoloured ..	10	15	☐	☐
		p. Phosphor	10	15	☐	☐
699	**259**	4d multicoloured ..	10	15	☐	☐
		p. Phosphor	10	15	☐	☐
		Set of 4 (Ordinary) ..	1·00	50	☐	☐
		Set of 4 (Phosphor) ..	1·00	50	☐	☐
		First Day Cover (Ordinary) ..		6·50		☐
		First Day Cover (Phosphor)		6·50		☐
		Presentation Pack (Ordinary)	7·00			☐

England's World Cup Football Victory

1966 (18 Aug.)

700	**260**	4d multicoloured ..	20	20	☐	☐
		First Day Cover		2·00		☐

261 Jodrell Bank Radio Telescope **262** British Motor-cars

263 SR N6 Hovercraft **264** Windscale Reactor

British Technology

1966 (19 Sept.)

701	**261**	4d black and lemon	15	15	☐	☐
		p. Phosphor ..	15	15	☐	☐
702	**262**	6d red, blue and orange	15	15	☐	☐
		p. Phosphor ..	15	15	☐	☐
703	**263**	1s 3d multicoloured ..	30	40	☐	☐
		p. Phosphor ..	45	50	☐	☐
704	**264**	1s 6d multicoloured ..	50	45	☐	☐
		p. Phosphor ..	65	60	☐	☐
		Set of 4 (Ordinary) ..	1·00	1·00	☐	☐
		Set of 4 (Phosphor) ..	1·25	1·25	☐	☐
		First Day Cover (Ordinary) ..		3·00		☐
		First Day Cover (Phosphor)		3·00		☐
		Presentation Pack (Ordinary)	7·00			☐

265

266

267

268

269

270

The above show battle scenes, they were issued together *se-tenant* in horizontal strips of six within the sheet.

271 Norman Ship

272 Norman Horsemen attacking Harold's Troops

900th Anniversary of Battle of Hastings

1966 (14 Oct.) *Designs show scenes from Bayeux Tapestry.* Wmk **179** (*sideways on 1s 3d*)

705	**265**	4d multicoloured ..	10	15	☐	☐
		a. *Strip of 6*				
		Nos. 705/10	2·00	2·00	☐	☐
		p. *Phosphor* ..	10	25	☐	☐
		pa. *Strip of 6*				
		Nos. 705p/10p	2·00	2·00	☐	☐
706	**266**	4d multicoloured ..	10	15	☐	☐
		p. *Phosphor* ..	10	25	☐	☐
707	**267**	4d multicoloured ..	10	15	☐	☐
		p. *Phosphor* ..	10	25	☐	☐
708	**268**	4d multicoloured ..	10	15	☐	☐
		p. *Phosphor* ..	10	25	☐	☐
709	**269**	4d multicoloured ..	10	15	☐	☐
		p. *Phosphor* ..	10	25	☐	☐
710	**270**	4d multicoloured ..	10	15	☐	☐
		p. *Phosphor* ..	10	25	☐	☐
711	**271**	6d multicoloured ..	10	10	☐	☐
		p. *Phosphor* ..	10	10	☐	☐
712	**272**	1s 3d multicoloured ..	20	20	☐	☐
		p. *Phosphor* ..	20	20	☐	☐
		Set of 8 (Ordinary) ..	2·25	1·50	☐	☐
		Set of 8 (Phosphor)	2·25	1·90	☐	☐
		First Day Cover (Ordinary)		3·00		☐
		First Day Cover (Phosphor)		3·00		☐
		Presentation Pack (Ordinary)	7·00		☐	

273 King of the Orient

274 Snowman

Christmas

1966 (1 Dec.) Wmk **179** (*upright on* 1s 6d)

713	**273**	3d multicoloured ..	10	10	☐	☐
		p. *Phosphor* ..	10	10	☐	☐
714	**274**	1s 6d multicoloured ..	35	35	☐	☐
		p. *Phosphor* ..	35	35	☐	☐
		Set of 2 (Ordinary)	45	45	☐	☐
		Set of 2 (Phosphor)	45	45	☐	☐
		First Day Cover (Ordinary)		1·50		☐
		First Day Cover (Phosphor)		1·50		☐
		Presentation Pack (Ordinary)	7·00		☐	

275 Sea Freight

276 Air Freight

European Free Trade Association (EFTA)

1967 (20 Feb.)

715	**275**	9d multicoloured ..	15	15	☐	☐
		p. *Phosphor* ..	15	15	☐	☐
716	**276**	1s 6d multicoloured ..	30	30	☐	☐
		p. *Phosphor* ..	30	30	☐	☐
		Set of 2 (Ordinary)	40	40	☐	☐
		Set of 2 (Phosphor)	40	40	☐	☐
		First Day Cover (Ordinary)		1·50		☐
		First Day Cover (Phosphor)		1·50		☐
		Presentation Pack (Ordinary)	1·50		☐	

277 Hawthorn and Bramble

278 Larger Bindweed and Viper's Bugloss

279 Ox-eye Daisy, Coltsfoot and Buttercup

280 Bluebell, Red Campion and Wood Anemone

The above were issued together *se-tenant* in blocks of four within the sheet.

281 Dog Violet

282 Primroses

British Wild Flowers

1967 (24 APR.)

717	277	4d multicoloured ..	15	10	☐	☐
		a. Block of 4 Nos. 717/20 ..	1·25	1·25	☐	☐
		p. Phosphor ..	10	10	☐	☐
		pa. Block of 4 Nos. 717p/20p	1·00	1·00	☐	☐
718	278	4d multicoloured ..	15	10	☐	☐
		p. Phosphor ..	10	10	☐	☐
719	279	4d multicoloured ..	15	10	☐	☐
		p. Phosphor ..	10	10	☐	☐
720	280	4d multicoloured ..	15	10	☐	☐
		p. Phosphor ..	10	10	☐	☐
721	281	9d multicoloured ..	15	10	☐	☐
		p. Phosphor ..	10	10	☐	☐
722	282	1s 9d multicoloured ..	20	20	☐	☐
		p. Phosphor ..	30	20	☐	☐
		Set of 6 (Ordinary) ..	1·40	65	☐	☐
		Set of 6 (Phosphor) ..	1·25	65	☐	☐
		First Day Cover (Ordinary)		2·50	☐	
		First Day Cover (Phosphor)		2·50	☐	
		Presentation Pack (Ordinary)	3·00		☐	
		Presentation Pack (Phosphor)	3·00		☐	

283 (value at left)

284 (value at right)

I   II

Two types of the 2d.
I. Value spaced away from left side of stamp.
II. Value close to left side from new multi-positive. This results in the portrait appearing in the centre, thus conforming with the other values.

1967–69 *Two phosphor bands, except where otherwise stated. No wmk*

723	283	½d orange-brown	10	20	☐	☐
724		1d olive (2 bands)	10	10	☐	☐
725		1d olive (1 centre band)	25	30	☐	☐
726		2d lake-brown (Type I) (2 bands)	10	15	☐	☐
727		2d lake-brown (Type II) (2 bands)	15	15	☐	☐
728		2d lake-brown (Type II) (1 centre band) ..	40	50	☐	☐
729		3d violet (1 centre band) ..	10	10	☐	☐
730		3d violet (2 bands)	30	30	☐	☐
731		4d sepia (2 bands)	10	10	☐	☐
732		4d olive-brown (1 centre band) ..	10	10	☐	☐
733		4d vermilion (1 centre band) ..	10	10	☐	☐
734		4d vermilion (1 side band) ..	1·40	1·60	☐	☐
735		5d blue	10	10	☐	☐
736		6d purple	20	20	☐	☐
737	284	7d emerald	40	30	☐	☐
738		8d vermilion	15	30	☐	☐
739		8d turquoise-blue ..	45	50	☐	☐
740		9d green	50	30	☐	☐
741	283	10d drab	45	50	☐	☐
742		1s violet	40	30	☐	☐
743		1s 6d blue & dp blue ..	50	30	☐	☐
		c. Phosphorised paper	75	90	☐	☐
744		1s 9d orange & black	40	30	☐	☐
		Set of 16 (one of each value and colour)	3·00	3·25	☐	☐
		Presentation Pack (one of each value)	6·00		☐	
		Presentation Pack (German)	45·00		☐	

First Day Covers

5 June 1967	Nos. 731, 742, 744	1·40	☐
8 Aug. 1967	Nos. 729, 740, 743	1·40	☐
5 Feb. 1968	Nos. 723/4, 726, 736	75	☐
1 July 1968	Nos. 735, 737/8, 741	1·10	☐

No. 734 exists with phosphor band at the left or right.

285 'Master Lambton'
(Sir Thomas Lawrence)

286 'Mares and Foals in a
Landscape' (George Stubbs)

287 'Children Coming Out
of School' (L. S. Lowry)

288 Gipsy Moth IV

British Paintings

1967 (10 JULY) *Two phosphor bands. No wmk*

748	285	4d multicoloured ..	10	10	☐	☐
749	286	9d multicoloured ..	20	20	☐	☐
750	287	1s 6d multicoloured ..	35	25	☐	☐
		Set of 3	50	50	☐	
		First Day Cover		1·50	☐	
		Presentation Pack	5·50		☐	

Sir Francis Chichester's World Voyage

1967 (24 JULY) *Three phosphor bands. No wmk*

751	288	1s 9d multicoloured ..	25	25	☐	☐
		First Day Cover		1·00	☐	

289 Radar Screen

290 *Penicillium notatum*

291 'VC-10' Jet Engines

292 Television Equipment

British Discovery and Invention

1967 (19 SEPT.) *Two phosphor bands (except 4d, three bands). Wmk 179 (sideways on 1s 9d)*

752	289	4d yell, blk & verm..	10	10	☐	☐
753	290	1s multicoloured ..	10	10	☐	☐
754	291	1s 6d multicoloured ..	25	15	☐	☐
755	292	1s 9d multicoloured ..	30	20	☐	☐
		Set of 4	60	50	☐	☐
		First Day Cover		1·00		☐
		Presentation Pack	2·00			☐

NO WATERMARK. All the following issues are on unwatermarked paper unless stated.

293 'The Adoration of
the Shepherds'
(School of Seville)

294 'Madonna and
Child' (Murillo)

295 'The Adoration of the Shepherds'
(Louis Le Nain)

Christmas

1967 *Two phosphor bands (except 3d, one phosphor band)*

756	293	3d multicoloured (27 Nov.) ..	10	10	☐	☐
757	294	4d multicoloured (18 Oct.) ..	10	10	☐	☐
758	295	1s 6d multicoloured (27 Nov.) ..	35	35	☐	☐
		Set of 3	50	50	☐	☐
		First Day Covers (2)		1·00		☐

Gift Pack 1967

1967 (27 Nov.) *Comprises Nos. 715p/22p and 748/58*

	Gift Pack	2·50		☐

1967–68 *No wmk Perf 11×12*

759	166	2s 6d brown	40	50	☐	☐
760	167	5s red	1·00	1·00	☐	☐
761	168	10s blue	5·00	5·50	☐	☐
762	169	£1 black	4·00	4·00	☐	☐
		Set of 4	9·00	10·00	☐	☐

296 Tarr Steps, Exmoor

297 Aberfeldy Bridge

298 Menai Bridge

299 M4 Viaduct

British Bridges

1968 (29 APR.) *Two phosphor bands* ✓

763	296	4d multicoloured ..	10	10	☐	☐
764	297	9d multicoloured ..	10	10	☐	☐
765	298	1s 6d multicoloured ..	20	15	☐	☐
766	299	1s 9d multicoloured ..	25	30	☐	☐
		Set of 4	60	60	☐	☐
		First Day Cover		1·10	☐	
		Presentation Pack	2·00		☐	

300 'TUC' and Trades Unionists

301 Mrs Emmeline Pankhurst (statue)

302 Sopwith 'Camel' and 'Lightning' Fighters

303 Captain Cook's *Endeavour* and Signature

British Anniversaries. Events described on stamps

1968 (29 MAY) *Two phosphor bands*

767	300	4d multicoloured ..	10	10	☐	☐
768	301	9d violet, grey and black	10	10	☐	☐
769	302	1s multicoloured ..	20	20	☐	☐
770	303	1s 9d ochre and brown	25	25	☐	☐
		Set of 4	60	60	☐	☐
		First Day Cover		3·25	☐	
		Presentation Pack	3·00		☐	

304 'Queen Elizabeth I' (Unknown Artist)

305 'Pinkie' (Lawrence)

306 'Ruins of St Mary Le Port' (Piper)

307 'The Hay Wain' (Constable)

British Paintings

1968 (12 AUG.) *Two phosphor bands*

771	304	4d multicoloured ..	10	10	☐	☐
772	305	1s multicoloured ..	15	15	☐	☐
773	306	1s 6d multicoloured ..	20	20	☐	☐
774	307	1s 9d multicoloured ..	25	25	☐	☐
		Set of 4	60	60	☐	☐
		First Day Cover		1·00	☐	
		Presentation Pack	2·00		☐	
		Presentation Pack (German) ..	6·00		☑	

Gift Pack 1968

1968 (16 SEPT.) *Comprises Nos. 763/74*

Gift Pack	6·00		☐
Gift Pack (German)	24·00		☐

Collectors Pack 1968

1968 (16 SEPT.) *Comprises Nos. 752/8 and 763/74*

Collectors Pack	6·00	☐

308 Girl and Boy with Rocking Horse

309 Girl with Doll's House

310 Boy with Train Set

Christmas

1968 (25 Nov.) *Two phosphor bands (except 4d, one centre phosphor band)*

775	**308**	4d multicoloured ..	10	10	☐	☐
776	**309**	9d multicoloured ..	15	15	☐	☐
777	**310**	1s 6d multicoloured ..	25	25	☐	☐
		Set of 3	50	50	☐	☐
		First Day Cover		1·00		☐
		Presentation Pack	2·00		☑	
		Presentation Pack (German)	5·00		☐	

RMS Queen Elizabeth 2

311 *Queen Elizabeth 2*

312 Elizabethan Galleon

313 East Indiaman

Cutty Sark

314 *Cutty Sark*

SS Great Britain

315 *Great Britain*

The 9d and 1s values were arranged in horizontal strips of three and pairs respectively throughout the sheet.

RMS Mauretania

316 *Mauretania I*

British Ships

1969 (15 Jan.) *Two phosphor bands (except 5d, one hori. phosphor band, 1s, two vert phosphor bands at right)*

778	**311**	5d multicoloured	10	10	☐	☐
779	**312**	9d multicoloured	10	15	☐	☐
		a. Strip. Nos. 779/81	1·00	1·00	☐	☐
780	**313**	9d multicoloured	10	15	☐	☐
781	**314**	9d multicoloured	10	15	☐	☐
782	**315**	1s multicoloured	25	25	☐	☐
		a. Pair. Nos. 782/3	90	85	☐	☐
783	**316**	1s multicoloured	25	25	☐	☐
		Set of 6	1·75	90	☐	☐
		First Day Cover		3·25		☐
		Presentation Pack .. ☑ ..	3·00		☐	
		Presentation Pack (German)	22·00		☐	

317 'Concorde in Flight

318 Plan and Elevation Views

319 'Concorde's' Nose and Tail

320 (See also Type 359a)

First Flight of 'Concorde'

1969 (3 Mar.) *Two phosphor bands*

784	**317**	4d multicoloured ..	10	10	☐	☐
785	**318**	9d multicoloured ..	20	20	☐	☐
786	**319**	1s 6d deep blue, grey and light blue ..	30	30	☐	☐
		Set of 3	50	50	☐	☐
		First Day Cover		1·25		☐
		Presentation Pack ..	2·50		☐	
		Presentation Pack (German)	18·00		☐	

1969 (5 Mar.) *P 12*

787	**320**	2s 6d brown	50	30	☐	☐
788		5s lake	2·25	60	☐	☐
789		10s ultramarine ..	7·00	7·50	☐	☐
790		£1 black	3·00	1·60	☐	☐
		Set of 4	11·50	9·00	☐	☐
		First Day Cover .. .. ☑		15·00		☐
		Presentation Pack	18·00		☐	
		Presentation Pack (German)	45·00		☐	

321 Page from the *Daily Mail*, and Vickers 'Vimy' Aircraft

322 Europa and C.E.P.T. Emblems

323 I.L.O. Emblem

324 Flags of N.A.T.O. Countries

325 Vickers 'Vimy' Aircraft and Globe showing Flight

Anniversaries. Events described on stamps

1969 (2 APR.) *Two phosphor bands*

791	321	5d	multicoloured ..	10	10	☐	☐
792	322	9d	multicoloured ..	20	20	☐	☐
793	323	1s	claret, red and blue	20	20	☐	☐
794	324	1s 6d	multicoloured ..	20	20	☐	☐
795	325	1s 9d	olive, yellow and turquoise-green	25	25	☐	☐
		Set of 5		85	85	☐	☐
		First Day Cover ..			1·50		☐
		Presentation Pack		2·50		☐	
		Presentation Pack (German)		40·00		☐	

326 Durham Cathedral

327 York Minster

328 St Giles' Cathedral, Edinburgh

329 Canterbury Cathedral

The above were issued together *se-tenant* in blocks of four within the sheet.

330 St Paul's Cathedral

331 Liverpool Metropolitan Cathedral

British Architecture (Cathedrals)

1969 (28 MAY) *Two phosphor bands*

796	326	5d	multicoloured ..	10	10	☐	☐
		a Block of 4 Nos. 796/9 ..	85	1·00		☐	☐
797	327	5d	multicoloured ..	10	10	☐	☐
798	328	5d	multicoloured ..	10	10	☐	☐
799	329	5d	multicoloured ..	10	10	☐	☐
800	330	9d	multicoloured ..	15	15	☐	☐
801	331	1s 6d	multicoloured ..	15	15	☐	☐
		Set of 6		1·00	55	☐	☐
		First Day Cover ..			2·00		☐
		Presentation Pack		3·00		☐	
		Presentation Pack (German)		22·00		☐	

332 The King's Gate, Caernarvon Castle

333 The Eagle Tower, Caernarvon Castle

334 Queen Eleanor's Gate, Caernarvon Castle

335 Celtic Cross, Margam Abbey

The 5d values were printed *se-tenant* in strips of three throughout the sheet.

336 Prince Charles

337 Mahatma Gandhi

Investiture of H.R.H. The Prince of Wales

1969 (1 July) *Two phosphor bands*

802	**332**	5d multicoloured ..	10	10	☐	☐
		a. Strip of 3				
		Nos. 802/4 ..	70	75	☐	☐
803	**333**	5d multicoloured ..	10	10	☐	☐
804	**334**	5d multicoloured ..	10	10	☐	☐
805	**335**	9d multicoloured ..	20	10	☐	☐
806	**336**	1s black and gold	20	10	☐	☐
		Set of 5 ..	1·00	45	☐	☐
		First Day Cover		1·25		☐
		Presentation Pack	1·40		☐	
		Presentation Pack (German)	16·00		☐	

Gandhi Centenary Year

1969 (13 Aug.) *Two phosphor bands*

807	**337**	1s 6d multicoloured ..	30	30	☐	☐
		First Day Cover		1·00		☐

Collectors Pack 1969

1969 (15 Sept.) *Comprises Nos. 775/86 and 791/807*

	Collectors Pack	20·00	☐	

338 National Giro

339 Telecommunications

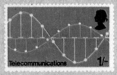

340 Telecommunications

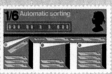

341 Automatic Sorting

British Post Office Technology

1969 (1 Oct.) *Two phosphor bands* Perf 13½ × 14

808	**338**	5d multicoloured ..	10	10	☐	☐
809	**339**	9d green, bl & blk ..	15	15	☐	☐
810	**340**	1s green, lav & blk ..	15	15	☐	☐
811	**341**	1s 6d multicoloured ..	40	40	☐	☐
		Set of 4	70	70	☐	☐
		First Day Cover		1·00		☐
		Presentation Pack	2·25		☐	

342 Herald Angel

343 The Three Shepherds

344 The Three Kings

Christmas

1969 (26 Nov.) *Two phosphor bands* (5d, 1s 6d) *or one centre band* (4d)

812	**342**	4d multicoloured ..	10	10	☐	☐
813	**343**	5d multicoloured ..	10	10	☐	☐
814	**344**	1s 6d multicoloured ..	30	30	☐	☐
		Set of 3	45	45	☐	☐
		First Day Cover		1·00		☐
		Presentation Pack	2·25		☐	

345 Fife Harling

346 Cotswold Limestone

347 Welsh Stucco

348 Ulster Thatch

British Rural Architecture

1970 (11 Feb.) *Two phosphor bands*

815	**345**	5d multicoloured ..	10	10	☐	☐
816	**346**	9d multicoloured ..	20	20	☐	☐
817	**347**	1s multicoloured ..	20	20	☐	☐
818	**348**	1s 6d multicoloured ..	35	35	☐	☐
		Set of 4	75	75	☐	☐
		First Day Cover		1·25		☐
		Presentation Pack	3·00		☐	

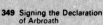

349 Signing the Declaration of Arbroath

350 Florence Nightingale attending Patients

351 Signing of International Co-operative Alliance

352 Pilgrims and *Mayflower*

353 Sir William Herschel, Francis Baily, Sir John Herschel and Telescope

Literary Anniversaries. *Events described on stamps*

1970 (3 June) *Two phosphor bands*

824	**354**	5d multicoloured ..	10	10	☐	☐
		a. *Block of 4 Nos.* 824/7 ..	90	90	☐	☐
825	**355**	5d multicoloured ..	10	10	☐	☐
826	**356**	5d multicoloured ..	10	10	☐	☐
827	**357**	5d multicoloured ..	10	10	☐	☐
828	**358**	1s 6d multicoloured ..	20	20	☐	☐
		Set of 5	1·00	55	☐	☐
		First Day Cover		2·00		☐
		Presentation Pack ..	3·00			☐

Anniversaries. *Events described on stamps*

1970 (1 Apr.) *Two phosphor bands*

819	**349**	5d multicoloured ..	10	10	☐	☐
820	**350**	9d multicoloured ..	15	15	☐	☐
821	**351**	1s multicoloured ..	25	15	☐	☐
822	**352**	1s 6d multicoloured ..	30	30	☐	☐
823	**353**	1s 9d multicoloured ..	30	30	☐	☐
		Set of 5	1·00	90	☐	☐
		First Day Cover		1·25		☐
		Presentation Pack ..	3·00			☐

359

359a (Value redrawn)

Decimal Currency

1970 (17 June)–**72** 10p *and some printings of the* 50p *were issued on phosphor paper Perf* 12

829	**359**	10p cerise ..	1·00	75	☐	☐
830		20p olive-green ..	70	15	☐	☐
831		50p ultramarine ..	1·50	40	☐	☐
831*b*	**359a**	£1 black ..	3·50	75	☐	☐
		Set of 4	6·00	1·75	☐	☐
829/31		*First Day Cover*		5·50		☐
831*b*		*First Day Cover* (6 Dec. 1972)		7·00		☐
829/31		*Presentation Pack*	7·00			☐
790 (*or* 831*b*), 830/1		*Presentation Pack* ..	8·00			☐

354 'Mr Pickwick and Sam' (*Pickwick Papers*)

355 'Mr and Mrs Micawber' (*David Copperfield*)

356 'David Copperfield and Betsy Trotwood' (*David Copperfield*)

357 'Oliver asking for more' (*Oliver Twist*)

358 'Grasmere' (from engraving by J Farrington, R.A.)

The 5d values were issued together *se-tenant* in blocks of four within the sheet.

360 Runners

361 Swimmers

362 Cyclists

Ninth British Commonwealth Games

1970 (15 July) *Two phosphor bands*   *Perf* $13\frac{1}{2} \times 14$ ✓

832	**360**	5d pink, emerald, greenish yellow & yellow-green		10	10	□	□
833	**361**	1s 6d greenish blue, lilac, brown and Prussian blue ..		50	50	□	□
834	**362**	1s 9d yellow-orange, lilac, salmon and red-brown ..		50	50	□	□
		Set of 3		1·00	1·00	□	□
		First Day Cover ..			1·25	□	
		Presentation Pack ..		2·50		□	

Collectors Pack 1970

1970 (14 Sept.) *Comprises Nos.* 808/28 *and* 832/4

Collectors Pack	..	.. ..	24·00	□

5d 9d 1/6
Philympia 1970 Philympia 1970 Philympia 1970
POSTAGE ONE SHILLING POSTAGE FOUR PENCE
ONE PENNY
1840 first engraved issue   1847 first embossed issue   1855 first surface printed issue

363 1d Black (1840)   **364** 1s Green (1847)   **365** 4d Carmine (1855)

'Philympia 70' Stamp Exhibition

1970 (18 Sept.) *Two phosphor bands*   *Perf* $14 \times 14\frac{1}{2}$ ✓

835	**363**	5d multicoloured ..		10	10	□	□
836	**364**	9d multicoloured ..		35	35	□	□
837	**365**	1s 6d multicoloured ..		40	40	□	□
		Set of 3		75	75	□	□
		First Day Cover			1·25	□	
		Presentation Pack		2·50		□	

366 Shepherds and Apparition of the Angel

367 Mary, Joseph, and Christ in the Manger

1/6

368 The Wise Men bearing Gifts

Christmas

1970 (25 Nov.) *Two phosphor bands* (5d, 1s 6d) *or one centre phosphor band* (4d)

838	**366**	4d multicoloured ..		10	10	□	□
839	**367**	5d multicoloured ..		10	10	□	□
840	**368**	1s 6d multicoloured ..		35	35	□	□
		Set of 3		50	50	□	□
		First Day Cover			1·00	□	
		Presentation Pack		2·50		□	

75p   **369**   75p   **369**a

Decimal Currency

1971-93. *Type* **369** ✓

(a) *Printed in photogravure by Harrison & Sons (except for some ptgs of Nos.* X879 *and* X913 *which were produced by Enschedé) with phosphor bands. Perf* 15×14.

X841	$\frac{1}{2}$p turq-bl (2 bands) ..		10	10	□	□
X842	$\frac{1}{2}$p turq-bl (1 side band) ..		60·00	25·00	□	□
X843	$\frac{1}{2}$p turquoise-blue (1 centre band)		30	20	□	□
X844	1p crimson (2 bands) ..		10	10	□	□
X845	1p crim (1 centre band) ..		20	20	□	□
X846	1p crimson ('all-over' phosphor)		20	20	□	□
X847	1p crimson (1 side band) ..		1·50	1·00	□	□
X848	$1\frac{1}{2}$p black (2 bands) ..		20	15	□	□
X849	2p myr-grn (face value as in T **369**) (2 bands) ..		20	10	□	□
X850	2p myr-grn (face value as in T **369**) 'all-over' phosphor ..		20	15	□	□
X851	$2\frac{1}{2}$p mag (1 centre band) ..		15	10	□	□
X852	$2\frac{1}{2}$p magenta (1 side band)		1·25	1·75	□	□
X853	$2\frac{1}{2}$p magenta (2 bands) ..		30	75	□	□
X854	$2\frac{1}{2}$p rose-red (2 bands) ..		50	75	□	□
X855	3p ultramarine (2 bands) ..		20	10	□	□
X856	3p ultram (1 centre band) ..		20	25	□	□
X857	3p bright magenta (2 bands) ..		30	25	□	□
X858	$3\frac{1}{2}$p olive-grey (2 bands) ..		30	30	□	□
X859	$3\frac{1}{2}$p ol-grey (1 centre band)		30	15	□	□

X860	3½p	purple-brown (1 centre band)	1·25	1·25	☐ ☐
X861	4p	ochre-brown (2 bands)	20	20	☐ ☐
X862	4p	greenish bl (2 bands)	1·50	1·50	☐ ☐
X863	4p	greenish blue (1 centre band)	1·00	1·00	☐ ☐
X864	4p	greenish blue (1 side band)	2·00	2·00	☐ ☐
X865	4½p	grey-blue (2 bands)	20	25	☐ ☐
X866	5p	pale violet (2 bands) ..	20	10	☐ ☐
X867	5p	claret (1 centre band)	1·60	1·60	☐ ☐
X868	5½p	violet (2 bands)	25	25	☐ ☐
X869	5½p	violet (1 centre band)	20	20	☐ ☐
X870	6p	light emerald (2 bands)	30	15	☐ ☐
X871	6½p	greenish bl (2 bands)	45	45	☐ ☐
X872	6½p	greenish blue (1 centre band)	30	15	☐ ☐
X873	6½p	greenish blue (1 side band)	60	55	☐ ☐
X874	7p	purple-brn (2 bands)	35	25	☐ ☐
X875	7p	purple-brown (1 centre band)	35	20	☐ ☐
X876	7p	purple-brown (1 side band)	60	75	☐ ☐
X877	7½p	chestnut (2 bands) ..	30	25	☐ ☐
X878	8p	rosine (2 bands) ..	25	20	☐ ☐
X879	8p	rosine (1 centre band)	25	15	☐ ☐
X880	8p	rosine (1 side band) ..	60	60	☐ ☐
X881	8½p	yellowish green (2 bands)	35	20	☐ ☐
X882	9p	yellow-orange and black (2 bands) ..	60	30	☐ ☐
X883	9p	deep violet (2 bands)	45	25	☐ ☐
X884	9½p	purple (2 bands) ..	45	30	☐ ☐
X885	10p	orange-brown and chestnut (2 bands)	40	30	☐ ☐
X886	10p	orange-brn (2 bands)	40	20	☐ ☐
X887	10p	orange-brown ('all-over' phosphor) ..	30	45	☐ ☐
X888	10p	orange-brown (1 centre band)	30	20	☐ ☐
X889	10p	orange-brown (1 side band)	75	75	☐ ☐
X890	10½p	yellow (2 bands) ..	40	30	☐ ☐
X891	10½p	blue (2 bands) ..	60	45	☐ ☐
X892	11p	brown-red (2 bands)	60	25	☐ ☐
X893	11½p	drab (1 centre band) ..	45	30	☐ ☐
X894	11½p	drab (1 side band) ..	60	60	☐ ☐
X895	12p	yellowish green (2 bands)	60	40	☐ ☐
X896	12p	bright emerald (1 centre band) ..	60	40	☐ ☐
X897	12p	bright emerald (1 side band)	75	75	☐ ☐
X898	12½p	light emerald (1 centre band)	45	25	☐ ☐
X899	12½p	light emerald (1 side band)	60	60	☐ ☐
X900	13p	pale chestnut (1 centre band)	45	35	☐ ☐
X901	13p	pale chestnut (1 side band)	60	60	☐ ☐
X902	14p	grey-blue (2 bands) ..	50	45	☐ ☐
X903	14p	dp bl (1 centre band)	60	40	☐ ☐
X904	14p	dp blue (1 side band)	2·50	1·75	☐ ☐
X905	15p	brt bl (1 centre band)	25	20	☐ ☐
X906	15p	brt blue (1 side band)	2·00	1·75	☐ ☐
X907	15½p	pale violet (2 bands) ..	45	45	☐ ☐
X908	16p	olive-drab (2 bands)	85	1·25	☐ ☐
X909	17p	grey-blue (2 bands) ..	75	75	☐ ☐
X910	17p	dp bl (1 centre band)	50	50	☐ ☐
X911	17p	dp bl (1 side band) ..	1·00	1·00	☐ ☐
X912	18p	dp ol-grey (2 bands)	75	75	☐ ☐
X913	18p	bright green (1 centre band)	30	35	☐ ☐
X914	19p	bright orange-red (2 bands)	1·25	1·25	☐ ☐
X915	20p	dull purple (2 bands)	90	40	☐ ☐
X916	20p	brownish black (2 bands)	1·00	1·00	☐ ☐
X917	22p	bright orange-red (2 bands)	1·00	1·00	☐ ☐
X918	26p	rosine (2 bands) ..	6·00	6·00	☐ ☐
X919	31p	purple (2 bands) ..	8·00	8·00	☐ ☐
X920	34p	ochre-brown (2 bands)	7·00	7·00	☐ ☐
X921	50p	ochre-brown (2 bands)	1·75	40	☐ ☐
X922	50p	ochre (2 bands)	4·50	4·50	☐ ☐

(b) Printed in photogravure by Harrison and Sons on phosphorised paper. Perf 15 × 14

X924	½p	turquoise-blue	10	10	☐ ☐
X925	1p	crimson	10	10	☐ ☐
X926	2p	myrtle-green (face value as in T **369**)	10	10	☐ ☐
X927	2p	deep green (smaller value as in T **369a**)	10	10	☐ ☐
X928	2p	myr-grn (smaller value as in T **369a**)	1·00	75	☐ ☐
X929	2½p	rose-red	20	20	☐ ☐
X930	3p	bright magenta ..	20	20	☐ ☐
X931	3½p	purple-brown ..	45	45	☐ ☐
X932	4p	greenish blue ..	25	20	☐ ☐
X933	4p	new blue	10	10	☐ ☐
X934	5p	pale violet	30	25	☐ ☐
X935	5p	dull red-brown ..	10	10	☐ ☐
X936	6p	olive-yellow	10	15	☐ ☐
X937	7p	brownish red	1·25	1·50	☐ ☐
X938	8½p	yellowish green ..	30	55	☐ ☐
X939	10p	orange-brown ..	30	20	☐ ☐
X940	10p	dull orange	15	15	☐ ☐
X941	11p	brown-red	75	75	☐ ☐
X942	11½p	ochre-brown	50	45	☐ ☐
X943	12p	yellowish green ..	45	40	☐ ☐
X944	13p	olive-grey	60	45	☐ ☐
X945	13½p	purple-brown ..	65	60	☐ ☐
X946	15p	grey-blue	50	40	☐ ☐
X947	15p	ultramarine	50	40	☐ ☐
X948	15½p	pale violet	50	40	☐ ☐
X949	16p	olive-drab	60	30	☐ ☐
X950	16½p	pale chestnut ..	85	75	☐ ☐
X951	17p	light emerald ..	70	40	☐ ☐
X952	17p	grey-blue	50	40	☐ ☐
X953	17½p	pale chestnut ..	80	80	☐ ☐
X954	18p	deep violet	70	75	☐ ☐
X955	18p	deep olive-grey ..	70	60	☐ ☐
X956	19p	bright orange-red ..	60	40	☐ ☐

X957	19½p olive-grey	1·75	1·50	□ □
X958	20p dull purple	1·25	20	□ □
X959	20p turquoise-green ..	30	35	□ □
X960	20p brownish black ..	50	40	□ □
X961	20½p ultramarine ..	1·00	85	□ □
X962	22p blue	80	45	□ □
X963	22p yellow-green	60	55	□ □
X964	22p bright orange-red ..	60	50	□ □
X965	23p brown-red	1·10	60	□ □
X966	23p bright green	80	40	□ □
X967	24p violet	1·40	85	□ □
X968	24p Indian red	1·25	80	□ □
X969	24p chestnut	40	45	□ □
X970	25p purple	90	90	□ □
X971	26p rosine	90	30	□ □
X972	26p drab	70	70	□ □
X973	27p chestnut	1·00	85	□ □
X974	27p violet	75	75	□ □
X975	28p deep violet.	90	90	□ □
X976	28p ochre	75	75	□ □
X977	28p deep bluish grey ..	45	50	□ □
X978	29p ochre-brown	2·00	1·25	□ □
X979	29p deep mauve	1·50	75	□ □
X980	30p deep olive-grey ..	80	50	□ □
X981	31p purple	1·25	1·25	□ □
X982	31p ultramarine	1·00	90	□ □
X983	32p greenish blue	1·00	1·00	□ □
X984	33p light emerald	90	80	□ □
X985	34p ochre-brown	1·25	80	□ □
X986	34p deep bluish grey ..	1·00	90	□ □
X987	34p deep mauve	90	60	□ □
X988	35p sepia	1·25	75	□ □
X989	35p yellow	90	60	□ □
X990	37p rosine	1·25	85	□ □
X991	39p bright mauve	1·00	65	□ □

(c) *Printed in photogravure by Harrison and Sons on ordinary paper. Perf* 15 × 14

X992	50p ochre-brown	1·25	80	□ □
X993	75p grey-black (smaller values as T **369***a*) ..	1·75	1·25	□ □

(d) *Printed in photogravure by Harrison and Sons on ordinary paper or phosphorised paper. Perf* 15 × 14

X994	50p ochre	75	45	□ □

(e) *Printed in lithography by John Waddington. Perf* 14.

X996	4p greenish blue (2 bands)	20	25	□ □
X997	4p greenish blue (phosphorised paper)	35	20	□ □
X998	20p dull purple (2 bands)	1·00	40	□ □
X999	20p dull purple (phosphorised paper)	1·25	40	□ □

(f) *Printed in lithography by Questa. Perf* 14 (*Nos* X1000, X1003/4 *and* X1023) *or* 15 × 14 (*others*)

X1000	2p emerald-green (face value as in T **369**) (phosphorised paper)	20	20	□ □
	a Perf 15 × 14 ..	30	20	□ □

X1001	2p bright grn and dp grn (smaller value as in T **369***a*) (phosphorised paper)	1·00	60	□ □
X1002	4p greenish blue (phosphorised paper)	50	50	□ □
X1003	5p light violet (phosphorised paper)	40	20	□ □
X1004	5p claret (phosphorised paper)	50	20	□ □
	a Perf 15 × 14 ..	50	25	□ □
X1005	13p pale chest (1 centre band)	70	70	□ □
X1006	13p pale chest (1 side band)	80	80	□ □
X1007	14p dp bl (1 centre band) ..	1·40	1·00	□ □
X1008	17p dp bl (1 centre band)	1·25	1·25	□ □
X1009	18p deep olive-grey (phosphorised paper)	1·00	1·00	□ □
X1010	18p dp ol-grey (2 bands)	4·50	4·50	□ □
X1011	18p bright green (1 centre band)	75	75	□ □
X1012	18p bright green (1 side band)	1·50	1·50	□ □
X1013	19p bright orange-red (phosphorised paper)	1·50	1·50	□ □
X1014	20p dull purple (phosphorised paper)	1·25	1·25	□ □
X1015	22p yell-grn (2 bands) ..	5·50	5·50	□ □
X1016	22p bright.orange-red (phosphorised paper)	1·00	1·00	□ □
X1017	24p chestnut (phosphorised paper) ·	80	60	□ □
X1018	24p chestnut (2 bands) ..	1·75	1·75	□ □
X1019	33p light emerald (phosphorised paper)	2·00	2·00	□ □
X1020	33p light emer (2 bands)	1·00	1·00	□ □
X1021	34p ochre-brn (2 bands)	5·50	5·50	□ □
X1022	39p brt mauve (2 bands)	2·00	2·00	□ □
X1023	75p black (face value as T **369**) (ordinary paper)	3·00	1·50	□ □
	a Perf 15 × 14	3·50	3·00	□ □
X1024	75p brownish grey and black (smaller value as T **369***a*) (ordinary paper)	9·00	5·00	□ □

(g) *Printed in lithography by Walsall. Perf* 14

X1050	2p deep green (phosphorised paper)	50	50	□ □
X1051	14p deep blue (1 side band)	2·50	2·50	□ □
X1052	19p bright orange-red (2 bands)	1·25	1·25	□ □
X1053	24p chestnut (phosphorised paper)	70	50	□ □
X1054	29p deep mauve (2 bands)	3·75	3·75	□ □
X1055	29p deep mauve (phosphorised paper)	3·50	3·50	□ □
X1056	31p ultramarine (phosphorised paper)	1·25	1·25	□ □
X1057	33p light emerald (phosphorised paper)	1·00	75	□ □
X1058	39p bright mauve (phosphorised paper)	1·00	75	□ □

Presentation Pack (*contains* ½p
(X841), 1p (X844), 1½p (X848), 2p
(X849), 2½p (X851), 3p (X855), 3½p
(X858), 4p (X861), 5p (X866), 6p
(X870), 7½p (X877), 9p (X882))   4·00   ☐

Presentation Pack ('Scandinavia 71')
(*contents as above*)   ..   ..   ..   32·00   ☐

Presentation Pack (*contains* ½p
(X841), 1p (X844), 1½p (X848), 2p
(X849), 2½p (X851), 3p (X855 *or*
X856), 3½p (X858 *or* X859), 4p
(X861), 4½p (X865), 5p (X866), 5½p
(X868 *or* X869), 6p (X870), 6½p
(X871 *or* X872), 7p (X874), 7½p
(X877), 8p (X878), 9p (X882), 10p
(X885))   ..   ..   4·00   ☐

Presentation Pack (*contains* ½p
(X841), 1p (X844), 1½p (X848), 2p
(X849), 2½p (X851), 3p (X856), 5p
(X866), 6½p (X872), 7p (X874 *or*
X875), 7½p (X877), 8p (X878), 8½p
(X881), 9p (X883), 9½p (X884) 10p
(X886), 10½p (X890), 11p (X892)
20p (X915), 50p (X921))   ..   ..   5·00   ☐

Presentation Pack (*contains* 2½p
(X929), 3p (X930), 4p (X996),
10½p (X891), 11½p (X893), 11½p
(X942), 12p (X943), 13p (X944),
13½p (X945), 14p (X946), 15p
(X947), 15½p (X948), 17p (X951),
17½p (X953), 18p (X954), 22p
(X962), 25p (X970), 75p (X1023))   16·00   ☐

Presentation Pack (*Contains* ½p
(X924), 1p (X925), 2p (X1000), 3p
(X930), 3½p (X931), 4p (X997), 5p
(X1004), 10p (X888), 12½p
(X898), 16p (X949), 16½p (X950),
17p (X952), 20p (X999), 20½p
(X961), 23p (X965), 26p (X971),
28p (X975), 31p (X981), 50p
(X992), 75p (X1023))   ..   ..   ..   22·00   ☐

Presentation Pack (*contains* ½p
(X924), 1p (X925), 2p (X1000a),
3p (X930), 4p (X997), 5p
(X1004a), 10p (X939), 13p
(X900), 16p (X949), 17p (X952),
18p (X955), 20p (X999), 22p
(X963), 24p (X967), 26p (X971),
28p (X975), 31p (X981), 34p
(X985), 50p (X992), 75p
(X1023a))   ..   ..   20·00   ☐

Presentation Pack (*contains* 1p
(X925), 2p (X1000a), 3p (X930),
4p (X997), 5p (X1004a), 7p
(X937), 10p (X939), 12p (X896),

13p (X900), 17p (X952), 18p
(X955), 20p (X999), 22p (X963),
24p (X967), 26p (X971), 28p
(X975), 31p (X981), 34p (X985),
50p (X992), 75p (X1023a))   ..   ..   16·00   ☐

Presentation Pack (*contains* 14p
(X903), 19p (X956), 20p (X959),
23p (X966), 27p (X973), 28p
(X976), 32p (X983), 35p (X988))   9·00   ☐

Presentation Pack (*contains* 15p
(X905), 20p (X960), 24p (X968),
29p (X979), 30p (X980), 34p
(X986), 37p (X990)   ..   ..   ..   7·00   ☐

Presentation Pack (*contains* 10p
(X940), 17p (X910), 22p (X964),
26p (X972), 27p (X974), 31p
(X982), 33p (X984)   ..   ..   ..   6·00   ☐

Presentation Pack (*contains* 1p
(X925), 2p (X927), 3p (X930), 4p
(X933), 5p (X935), 10p (X940),
17p (X910), 20p (X959), 22p
(X964), 26p (X972), 27p (X974),
30p (X980), 31p (X982), 32p
(X983), 33p (X984), 37p (X990),
50p (X994), 75p (X993))   ..   ..   7·00   ☐

Presentation Pack (*contains* 6p
(X936), 18p (X913), 24p (X969),
28p (X977), 34p (X987), 35p
(X989), 39p (X991))   ..   ..   ..   3·25   ☐

First Day Covers

15 Feb. 1971	½p, 1p, 1½p, 2p, 2½p, 3p, 3½p, 4p, 5p, 6p, 7½p, 9p (*Nos.* X841, X844, X848/9, X851, X855, X858, X861, X866, X870, X877, X882) (*Covers carry* "POSTING DELAYED BY THE POST OFFICE STRIKE 1971" *cachet*) ..	2·25	☐
11 Aug. 1971	10p (*No.* X885)	1·00	☐
24 Oct. 1973	4½p, 5½p, 8p (*Nos.* X865 X868, X878)	1·00	☐
4 Sept. 1974	6½p (*No.* X871)	1·10	☐
15 Jan. 1975	7p (*No.* X874)	75	☐
24 Sept. 1975	8½p (*No.* X881)	1·25	☐
25 Feb. 1976	9p, 9½p, 10p, 10½p, 11p, 20p (*Nos.* X883/4, X886, X890, X892, X915)	2·75	☐
2 Feb. 1977	50p (*No.* X921)	2·25	☐
26 April. 1978	10½p (*No.* X891)	1·00	☐
15 Aug. 1979	11½p, 13p, 15p (*Nos.* X942, X944, X947)	2·00	☐
30 Jan. 1980	4p, 12p, 13½p, 17p, 17½p, 75p (*Nos.* X996, X943, X945, X951, X953, X1023)	4·50	☐
22 Oct. 1980	3p, 22p, (*Nos.* X930, X962)	1·00	☐

14 Jan. 1981	$2\frac{1}{2}p$, $11\frac{1}{2}p$, 14p, $15\frac{1}{2}p$, 18p, 25p (Nos. X929, X893, X946, X948, X954, X970)	2·25	☐
27 Jan. 1982	5p, $12\frac{1}{2}p$, $16\frac{1}{2}p$, $19\frac{1}{2}p$, 26p, 29p (Nos. X1004, X898, X950, X957, X971, X978) ..	3·25	☐
30 March 1983	$3\frac{1}{2}p$, 16p, 17p, $20\frac{1}{2}p$, 23p, 28p, 31p (Nos. X931, X949, X952, X961, X965, X975, X981)	4·50	☐
28 Aug. 1984	13p, 18p, 22p, 24p, 34p (Nos. X900, X955, X963, X967, X985)	5·00	☐
23 Aug. 1988	14p, 19p, 20p, 23p, 27p, 28p, 32p, 35p (Nos. X903, X956, X959, X966, X973, X976, X983, X988)	5·50	☐
26 Sept. 1989	15p, 20p, 24p, 29p, 30p, 34p, 37p (Nos. X905, X960, X968, X979/80, X986, X990) ..	4·00	☐
4 Sept. 1990	10p, 17p, 22p, 26p, 27p, 31p, 33p (Nos. X940, X910, X964, X972, X974, X982, X984)	3·50	☐
10 Sept. 1991	6p, 18p, 24p, 28p, 34p, 35p, 39p (Nos. X936, X913, X969, X977, X987, X989, X991) ..	4·50	☐

PHOSPHOR BANDS See notes on page 15.
Phosphor bands are applied to the stamps, after the design has been printed, by a separate cylinder. On issues with "all-over" phosphor the "band" covers the entire stamp. Parts of the stamp covered by phosphor bands, or the entire surface for "all-over" phosphor versions, appear matt.
Nos. X847, X852, X864, X873, X876, X880, X889, X894, X897, X899, X901, X906, X911, X1006 and X1012 exist with the phosphor band at the left or right of the stamp.

PHOSPHORISED PAPER. First introduced as an experiment for a limited printing of the 1s 6d value (No. 743c) in 1969 this paper has the phosphor, to activate the automatic sorting machinery, added to the paper coating before the stamps were printed. Issues on this paper have a completely shiny surface. Although not adopted after this first trial further experiments on the $8\frac{1}{2}$p in 1976 led to this paper being used for new printings of current values.

For similar stamps, but with elliptical perforations see Nos. Y1667/1752 in 1993.

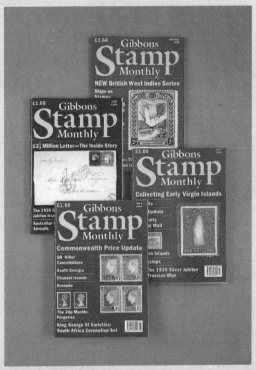

370 'A Mountain Road' (T. P. Flanagan)

371 'Deer's Meadow' (Tom Carr)

372 'Slieve na brock' (Colin Middleton)

'Ulster '71' Paintings

1971 (16 JUNE) *Two phosphor bands* ✓

881	370	3p multicoloured ..	10	10	☐	☐
882	371	7½p multicoloured ..	50	50	☐	☐
883	372	9p multicoloured ..	50	50	☐	☐
		Set of 3	1·00	1·00	☐	☐
		First Day Cover		1·75		☐
		Presentation Pack	5·00		☐	

373 John Keats (150th Death Anniv)

374 Thomas Gray (Death Bicentenary)

375 Sir Walter Scott (Birth Bicentenary)

Literary Anniversaries. Events described above

1971 (28 JULY) *Two phosphor bands*

884	373	3p black, gold & bl ..	10	10	☐	☐
885	374	5p blk, gold & olive	50	50	☐	☐
886	375	7½p black, gold & brn	50	50	☐	☐
		Set of 3	1·00	1·00	☐	☐
		First Day Cover		1·50		☐
		Presentation Pack	5·00		☐	

376 Servicemen and Nurse of 1921

377 Roman Centurion

378 Rugby Football, 1871

British Anniversaries. Events described on stamps

1971 (25 AUG.) *Two phosphor bands* ✓

887	376	3p multicoloured ..	10	10	☐	☐
888	377	7½p multicoloured ..	50	50	☐	☐
889	378	9p multicoloured ..	50	50	☐	☐
		Set of 3	1·00	1·00	☐	☐
		First Day Cover		1·50		☐
		Presentation Pack	5·00		☐	

379 Physical Sciences Building, University College of Wales, Aberystwyth

380 Faraday Building, Southampton University

381 Engineering Department, Leicester University

382 Hexagon Restaurant, Essex University

British Architecture (Modern University Buildings)

1971 (22 Sept.) *Two phosphor bands* ✓

890	**379**	3p multicoloured ..	10	10	☐	☐
891	**380**	5p multicoloured ..	20	20	☐	☐
892	**381**	7½p ochre, black and				
		purple-brown. ..	50	50	☐	☐
893	**382**	9p multicoloured ..	90	90	☐	☐
	Set of 4		1·50	1·50	☐	☐
	First Day Cover			1·75		☐
	Presentation Pack		5·00			☐

Collectors Pack 1971

1971 (29 Sept.) *Comprises Nos. 835/40 and 881/93*

	Collectors Pack	28·00	☐

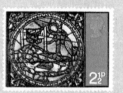

383 'Dream of the Wise Men'

384 'Adoration of the Magi'

385 'Ride of the Magi'

Christmas

1971 (13 Oct.) *Two phosphor bands (3p, 7½p) or one centre phosphor band (2½p)* ✓

894	**383**	2½p multicoloured ..	10	10	☐	☐
895	**384**	3p multicoloured ..	10	10	☐	☐
896	**385**	7½p multicoloured ..	90	90	☐	☐
	Set of 3		1·00	1·00	☐	☐
	First Day Cover			1·50		☐
	Presentation Pack		4·00			☐

386 Sir James Clark Ross

387 Sir Martin Frobisher

388 Henry Hudson

389 Capt. Robert F. Scott

British Polar Explorers

1972 (16 Feb.) *Two phosphor bands* ✓

897	**386**	3p multicoloured ..	10	10	☐	☐
898	**387**	5p multicoloured ..	20	20	☐	☐
899	**388**	7½p multicoloured ..	50	50	☐	☐
900	**389**	9p multicoloured ..	90	90	☐	☐
	Set of 4		1·50	1·50	☐	☐
	First Day Cover			2·00		☐
	Presentation Pack ..		4·50			☐

390 Statuette of Tutankhamun

391 19th-century Coastguard

392 Ralph Vaughan Williams and Score

Anniversaries. Events described on stamps

1972 (26 Apr.) *Two phosphor bands* ✓

901	**390**	3p multicoloured ..	10	10	☐	☐
902	**391**	7½p multicoloured ..	50	50	☐	☐
903	**392**	9p multicoloured ..	50	50	☐	☐
	Set of 3		1·00	1·00	☐	☐
	First Day Cover			1·75		☐
	Presentation Pack		4·00			☐

393 St Andrew's, Greensted-
juxta-Ongar, Essex

394 All Saints, Earls
Barton, Northants

395 St Andrew's,
Letheringsett, Norfolk

396 St Andrew's,
Helpringham, Lincs

397 St Mary the Virgin, Huish
Episcopi, Somerset

British Architecture (Village Churches)

1972 (21 June) *Two phosphor bands* ✔

904	**393**	3p multicoloured ..	10	10	☐	☐
905	**394**	4p multicoloured ..	20	20	☐	☐
906	**395**	5p multicoloured ..	20	25	☐	☐
907	**396**	7½p multicoloured ..	70	80	☐	☐
908	**397**	9p multicoloured ..	75	90	☐	☐
	Set of 5		1·75	2·00	☐	☐
	First Day Cover			3·00		☐
	Presentation Pack		5·00			☐

'Belgica '72' Souvenir Pack

1972 (24 June) *Comprises Nos. 894/6 and 904/8*

Souvenir Pack	9·50		☐

398 Microphones, 1924–69

399 Horn Loudspeaker

400 TV Camera, 1972

401 Oscillator and Spark
Transmitter, 1897

Broadcasting Anniversaries. Events described on stamps

1972 (13 Sept.) *Two phosphor bands* ✔

909	**398**	3p multicoloured ..	10	10	☐	☐
910	**399**	5p multicoloured ..	15	20	☐	☐
911	**400**	7½p multicoloured ..	60	60	☐	☐
912	**401**	9p multicoloured ..	60	60	☐	☐
	Set of 4		1·25	1·25	☐	☐
	First Day Cover			2·00		☐
	Presentation Pack		3·50		☐

402 Angel holding Trumpet

403 Angel playing Lute

404 Angel playing Harp

Christmas

1972 (18 Oct.) *Two phosphor bands (3p, 7½p) or one centre* ✓
phosphor band (2½p)

913	**402**	2½p multicoloured ..	10	15	☐	☐
914	**403**	3p multicoloured ..	10	15	☐	☐
915	**404**	7½p multicoloured ..	90	80	☐	☐
		Set of 3	1·00	1·00	☐	☐
		First Day Cover		1·25		☐
		Presentation Pack	2·75		☐	

405 Queen Elizabeth II
and Prince Philip

406 'Europe'

Royal Silver Wedding

1972 (20 Nov.) *3p 'all-over' phosphor, 20p without* ✓
phosphor

916	**405**	3p brownish black, deep blue and silver ..	20	20	☐	☐
917		20p brownish black, reddish purple and silver ..	80	80	☐	☐
		Set of 2	1·00	1·00	☐	☐
		First Day Cover		1·25		☐
		Presentation Pack	2·25		☐	
		Presentation Pack (Japanese)	3·50		☐	
		Souvenir Book	3·00		☐	
		Gutter Pair (3p)	1·00		☐	
		Traffic Light Gutter Pair (3p)	22·00		☐	

Collectors Pack 1972

1972 (20 Nov.) *Comprises Nos.* 897/917

Collectors Pack	28·00	☐

Nos. 920/1 were issued horizontally *se-tenant* throughout the sheet.

Britain's Entry into European Communities

1973 (3 Jan.) *Two phosphor bands* ✓

919	**406**	3p multicoloured ..	10	10	☐	☐
920		5p multicoloured (blue jigsaw) ..	25	35	☐	☐
		a. Pair. Nos. 920/1	1·10	1·25	☐	☐
921		5p multicoloured (green jigsaw)	25	35	☐	☐
		Set of 3	1·50	70	☐	☐
		First Day Cover		1·50		☐
		Presentation Pack	2·25		☐	

9p

Oak *Quercus robur*   **407** Oak Tree

British Trees (1st issue)

1973 (28 Feb.) *Two phosphor bands* ✓

922	**407**	9p multicoloured ..	50	50	☐	☐
		First Day Cover		1·00		☐
		Presentation Pack	2·25		☐	

See also No. 949.

408 David Livingstone

409 H. M. Stanley

The above were issued horizontally *se-tenant* throughout the sheet.

410 Sir Francis Drake

411 Sir Walter Raleigh

412 Charles Sturt

41

British Explorers

1973 (18 APR.) *'All-over' phosphor*

923	**408**	3p multicoloured ..	25	20	□	□
		a. Pair. Nos. 923/4	1·00	1·75	□	□
924	**409**	3p multicoloured ..	25	20	□	□
925	**410**	5p multicoloured ..	20	30	□	□
926	**411**	7½p multicoloured ..	20	30	□	□
927	**412**	9p multicoloured ..	25	40	□	□
		Set of 5	1·50	1·25	□	□
		First Day Cover		2·00	□	
		Presentation Pack	3·50		□	

413

414

415

County Cricket 1873–1973

1973 (16 MAY) *Designs show sketches of W. G. Grace by Harry Furniss. Queen's head in gold. 'All-over' phosphor*

928	**413**	3p black and brown	10	10	□	□
929	**414**	7½p black and green	70	70	□	□
930	**415**	9p black and blue	90	90	□	□
		Set of 3	1·50	1·50	□	□
		First Day Cover		2·00	□	
		Presentation Pack	3·50		□	
		Souvenir Book	6·25		□	
		PHQ Card (No. 928)	50·00	£140	□	□

For full information on all future British issues, collectors should write to the British Post Office Philatelic Bureau, 20 Brandon Street, Edinburgh EH3 5TT

416 'Self-portrait' (Sir Joshua Reynolds)

417 'Self-portrait' (Sir Henry Raeburn)

418 'Nelly O'Brien' (Sir Joshua Reynolds)

419 'Rev R. Walker (The Skater)' (Sir Henry Raeburn)

Artistic Anniversaries. Events described on stamps

1973 (4 JULY) *'All-over' phosphor*

931	**416**	3p multicoloured ..	10	10	□	□
932	**417**	5p multicoloured ..	20	25	□	□
933	**418**	7½p multicoloured ..	45	40	□	□
934	**419**	9p multicoloured ..	50	50	□	□
		Set of 4	1·10	1·10	□	□
		First Day Cover		1·75		□
		Presentation Pack	2·75		□	

420 Court Masque Costumes

421 St Paul's Church, Covent Garden

422 Prince's Lodging, Newmarket

423 Court Masque Stage Scene

The 3p and 5p values were printed horizontally *se-tenant* within the sheet.

400th Anniversary of the Birth of Inigo Jones

1973 (15 Aug.) *'All-over' phosphor*

935	**420**	3p deep mauve, black and gold ..	10	15	☐	☐
		a. *Pair. Nos.* 935/6	35	40	☐	☐
936	**421**	3p deep brown, black and gold ..	10	15	☐	☐
937	**422**	5p blue, black and gold ..	40	45	☐	☐
		a. *Pair. Nos.* 937/8	1·50	1·50	☐	☐
938	**423**	5p grey-olive, black and gold	40	45	☐	☐
		Set of 4	1·60	1·10	☐	☐
		First Day Cover .. .. ✓ ..		2·00		☐
		Presentation Pack .. ✓	3·50		☐	
		PHQ Card (*No.* 936)	£125	70·00	☐	☐

424 Palace of Westminster seen from Whitehall

425 Palace of Westminster seen from Millbank

19th Commonwealth Parliamentary Conference

1973 (12 Sept.) *'All-over' phosphor*

939	**424**	8p black, grey and pale buff	50	60	☐	☐
940	**425**	10p gold and black	50	40	☐	☐
		Set of 2	1·00	1·00	☐	☐
		First Day Cover .. .. ✓		1·25		☐
		Presentation Pack .. ✓ ..	2·00		☐	
		Souvenir Book	5·00		☐	
		PHQ Card (*No.* 939) ..	35·00	90·00	☐	☐

2S

426 Princess Anne and Captain Mark Phillips

Royal Wedding

1973 (14 Nov.) *'All-over' phosphor*

941	**426**	3½p violet and silver	10	10	☐	☐
942		20p brown and silver	90	90	☐	☐
		Set of 2	1·00	1·00	☐	☐
		First Day Cover		1·25		☐
		Presentation Pack ✓ ..	2·00		☐	
		PHQ Card (*No.* 941)	8·00	22·00	☐	☐
		Set of 2 Gutter Pairs	6·00		☐	
		Set of 2 Traffic Light Gutter Pairs	£100		☐	

5 0 0

427

428

429

430

431

432 'Good King Wenceslas, the Page and Peasant'

The 3p values depict the carol 'Good King Wenceslas' and were printed horizontally *se-tenant* within the sheet.

Christmas

1973 (28 Nov.) *One phosphor band* (3p) *or 'all-over' phosphor* (3½p)

943	**427**	3p multicoloured ..	15	15	☐	☐
		a. *Strip of 5.* Nos. 943/7 ..	2·75	2·50	☐	☐
944	**428**	3p multicoloured ..	15	15	☐	☐
945	**429**	3p multicoloured ..	15	15	☐	☐
946	**430**	3p multicoloured ..	15	15	☐	☐
947	**431**	3p multicoloured ..	15	15	☐	☐
948	**432**	3½p multicoloured ..	15	15	☐	☐
		Set of 6	2·75	80	☐	☐
		First Day Cover .. .. ✓ ..		2·00		☐
		Presentation Pack .. ✓ ..	3·25		☐	

Collectors Pack 1973

1973 (28 Nov.) *Comprises Nos.* 919/48

	Collectors Pack	26·00	☐

433 Horse Chestnut

British Trees (2nd issue)

1974 (27 FEB.) *'All-over' phosphor*

949	**433**	10p multicoloured ..	·	50	50	□	□
		First Day Cover			1·00		□
		Presentation Pack	✓	2·25		□	✓
		PHQ Card		£100	60·00	□	□
		Gutter Pair		3·00		□	
		Traffic Light Gutter Pair ..		70·00		□	

£1·25

434 First Motor Fire-engine, 1904

435 Prize-winning Fire-engine, 1863

436 Steam Fire-engine, 1830

437 Fire-engine, 1766

200th Anniversary of Public Fire Services

1974 (24 APR.) *'All-over' phosphor*

950	**434**	3½p multicoloured ..	10	10	□	□
951	**435**	5½p multicoloured ..	25	25	□	□
952	**436**	8p multicoloured ..	35	35	□	□
953	**437**	10p multicoloured ..	40	40	□	□
		Set of 4	1·00	1·00	□	□
		First Day Cover		3·00		□
		Presentation Pack ✓	2·50		□	
		PHQ Card (No. 950)	£100	50·00	□	□
		Set of 4 Gutter Pairs ..	4·00		□	
		Set of 4 Traffic Light Gutter Pairs ..	70·00		□	

438 P & O Packet Peninsular, 1888

439 Farman Biplane, 1911

440 Airmail-blue Van and Postbox, 1930

441 Imperial Airways 'C' Class Flying-boat, 1937

Centenary of Universal Postal Union

1974 (12 JUNE) *'All-over' phosphor*

954	**438**	3½p multicoloured ..	10	10	□	□
955	**439**	5½p multicoloured ..	20	25	□	□
956	**440**	8p multicoloured ..	30	35	□	□
957	**441**	10p multicoloured ..	50	40	□	□
		Set of 4	1·00	1·00	□	□
		First Day Cover		1·25		□
		Presentation Pack ✓	2·00		□	
		Set of 4 Gutter Pairs ..	4·00		□	
		Set of 4 Traffic Light Gutter Pairs ..	50·00		□	

442 Robert the Bruce

443 Owain Glyndŵr

444 Henry the Fifth

445 The Black Prince

Medieval Warriors

1974 (10 JULY) *'All-over' phosphor*

958	**442**	4½p multicoloured ..	10	10	□	□
959	**443**	5½p multicoloured ..	20	20	□	□
960	**444**	8p multicoloured ..	40	40	□	□
961	**445**	10p multicoloured ..	40	40	□	□
		Set of 4	1·00	1·00	□	□
		First Day Cover		2·50		□
		Presentation Pack	3·50	✓	□	
		PHQ Cards (set of 4) ..	30·00	24·00	□	□
		Set of 4 Gutter Pairs ..	6·00		□	
		Set of 4 Traffic Light Gutter Pairs ..	75·00		□	

446 Churchill in Royal Yacht Squadron Uniform

447 Prime Minister, 1940

448 Secretary for War and Air. 1919

449 War Correspondent, South Africa, 1899

Birth Centenary of Sir Winston Churchill

1974 (9 Oct.) *Queen's head and inscription in silver. 'All-over' phosphor*

962	**446**	4½p green and blue	15	15	☐	☐
963	**447**	5½p grey and black	20	25	☐	☐
964	**448**	8p rose and lake ..	50	50	☐	☐
965	**449**	10p stone and brown	55	50	☐	☐
	Set of 4	.. .. ..	1·25	1·25	☐	☐
	First Day Cover			1·60	☐	
	Presentation Pack..	.. ..	1·75		☐	
	Souvenir Book	.. ..	2·50		☐	
	PHQ Card (No. 963)	..	7·00	12·00	☐	☐
	Set of 4 Gutter Pairs	..	4·00		☐	
	Set of 4 Traffic Light					
	Gutter Pairs	.. ..	50·00		☐	

450 'Adoration of the Magi' (York Minster, c. 1355)

451 'The Nativity' (St Helen's Church, Norwich, c. 1480)

452 'Virgin and Child' (Ottery St Mary Church, c. 1350)

453 'Virgin and Child' (Worcester Cathedral, c. 1224)

Christmas

1974 (27 Nov.) *Designs show church roof bosses, One phosphor band (3½p) or 'all-over' phosphor (others)*

966	**450**	3½p multicoloured ..	10	10	☐	☐
967	**451**	4½p multicoloured	10	10	☐	☐
968	**452**	8p multicoloured ..	45	45	☐	☐
969	**453**	10p multicoloured ..	50	50	☐	☐
	Set of 4	.. ..	1·00	1·00	☐	☐
	First Day Cover	..		1·25	☐	
	Presentation Pack	..	1·75		☐	
	Set of 4 Gutter Pairs	.. ..	4·00		☐	
	Set of 4 Traffic Light					
	Gutter Pairs	.. ..	50·00		☐	

Collectors Pack 1974

1974 (27 Nov.) *Comprises Nos 949/69*

	Collectors Pack	8·50	☐

454 Invalid in Wheelchair

Health and Handicap Funds

1975 (22 Jan.) *'All-over' phosphor*

970	**454**	4½p + 1½p azure and blue	25	25	☐	☐
	First Day Cover			1·00		☐
	Gutter Pair	.. ..	50		☐	
	Traffic Light Gutter Pair		1·00		☐	

455 'Peace – Burial at Sea'

456 'Snowstorm – Steamer off a Harbour's Mouth'

457 'The Arsenal, Venice'

458 'St Laurent'

Birth Bicentenary of J. M. W. Turner

1975 (19 Feb.) *'All-over' phosphor*

971	**455**	4½p multicoloured	10	10	☐	☐
972	**456**	5½p multicoloured	15	15	☐	☐
973	**457**	8p multicoloured	40	40	☐	☐
974	**458**	10p multicoloured	45	45	☐	☐
	Set of 4	.. ..	1·00	1·00	☐	☐
	First Day Cover	..		1·50		☐
	Presentation Pack	..	2·50		☐	
	PHQ Card (No. 972)		30·00	11·00	☐	☐
	Set of 4 Gutter Pairs	..	2·50		☐	
	Set of 4 Traffic Light					
	Gutter Pairs	.. ..	7·00		☐	

459 Charlotte Square, Edinburgh

460 The Rows, Chester

The above were printed horizontally *se-tenant* throughout the sheet.

461 Royal Observatory, Greenwich

462 St George's Chapel, Windsor

463 National Theatre, London

European Architectural Heritage Year

1975 (23 APR.) *'All-over' phosphor*

975	**459**	7p multicoloured	..	30	30	☐	☐
		a. Pair. Nos. 975/6		80	90	☐	☐
976	**460**	7p multicoloured	..	30	30	☐	☐
977	**461**	8p multicoloured	..	20	25	☐	☐
978	**462**	10p multicoloured	..	20	25	☐	☐
979	**463**	12p multicoloured	..	20	35	☐	☐
	Set of 5	.. .. ..		1·25	1·25	☐	
	First Day Cover	.. .. ..			2·00		☐
	Presentation Pack		..	3·00		☐	
	PHQ Cards (Nos. 975/7)		..	8·00	10·00	☐	☐
	Set of 5 Gutter Pairs		..	4·00		☐	
	Set of 5 Traffic Light Gutter Pairs	.. .. ..		20·00		☐	

464 Sailing Dinghies

465 Racing Keel Boats

466 Cruising Yachts

467 Multihulls

Sailing

1975 (11 JUNE) *'All-over' phosphor* ✓

980	**464**	7p multicoloured	..	20	20	☐	☐
981	**465**	8p multicoloured	..	30	30	☐	☐
982	**466**	10p multicoloured	..	30	30	☐	☐
983	**467**	12p multicoloured	..	35	35	☐	☐
	Set of 4	.. .. ..		1·00	1·00	☐	☐
	First Day Cover	.. ..			1·50		☐
	Presentation Pack		..	1·50		☐	
	PHQ Card (No. 981)		..	4·50	10·00	☐	☐
	Set of 4 Gutter Pairs		..	2·50		☐	
	Set of 4 Traffic Light Gutter Pairs	.. .. ..		25·00		☐	

468 Stephenson's Locomotion, 1825

469 Abbotsford, 1876

470 Caerphilly Castle, 1923

471 High Speed Train, 1975

150th Anniversary of Public Railways

1975 (13 AUG.) *'All-over' phosphor* ✓

984	**468**	7p multicoloured	..	20	20	☐	☐
985	**469**	8p multicoloured	..	25	25	☐	☐
986	**470**	10p multicoloured	..	30	30	☐	☐
987	**471**	12p multicoloured	..	35	35	☐	☐
	Set of 4	.. .. ..		1·00	1·00	☐	☐
	First Day Cover	.. ..			2·50		☐
	Presentation Pack		..	2·25		☐	
	Souvenir Book		..	3·00		☐	
	PHQ Cards (set of 4)		..	55·00	25·00	☐	☐
	Set of 4 Gutter Pairs		..	3·00		☐	
	Set of 4 Traffic Light Gutter Pairs	.. .. ..		12·00		☐	

472 Palace of Westminster

477 Angels with Harp and Lute

478 Angel with Mandolin

479 Angel with Horn

480 Angel with Trumpet

62nd Inter-Parliamentary Union Conference

1975 (3 Sept.) *'All-over' phosphor* ✔

988	**472**	12p multicoloured	50	50	☐	☐
		First Day Cover		1·00		☐
		Presentation Pack	1·25		☐	
		Gutter Pair	1·00		☐	
		Traffic Light Gutter Pair	3·00		☐	

473 Emma and Mr Woodhouse (*Emma*)

474 Catherine Morland (*Northanger Abbey*)

475 Mr Darcy (*Pride and Prejudice*)

476 Mary and Henry Crawford (*Mansfield Park*)

Birth Bicentenary of Jane Austen (Novelist)

1975 (22 Oct.) *'All-over' phosphor* ✔

989	**473**	8½p multicoloured	20	20	☐	☐
990	**474**	10p multicoloured	25	25	☐	☐
991	**475**	11p multicoloured	30	30	☐	☐
992	**476**	13p multicoloured	35	35	☐	☐
		Set of 4	1·00	1·00	☐	☐
		First Day Cover		1·25		☐
		Presentation Pack	2·00		☐	
		PHQ Cards (set of 4)	16·00	15·00	☐	☐
		Set of 4 Gutter Pairs	2·50		☐	
		Set of 4 Traffic Light Gutter Pairs	8·00		☐	

Christmas

1975 (26 Nov.) *One phosphor band (6½p), phosphor-inked (8½p) (background) or 'all-over' phosphor (others)*

993	**477**	6½p multicoloured	20	15	☐	☐
994	**478**	8½p multicoloured	20	20	☐	☐
995	**479**	11p multicoloured	30	35	☐	☐
996	**480**	13p multicoloured	40	40	☐	☐
		Set of 4	1·00	1·00	☐	☐
		First Day Cover		1·25		☐
		Presentation Pack	2·00		☐	
		Set of 4 Gutter Pairs	2·50		☐	
		Set of 4 Traffic Light Gutter Pairs	8·00		☐	

Collectors Pack 1975

1975 (26 Nov.) *Comprises Nos. 970/96*

	Collectors Pack	7·50	☐

481 Housewife

482 Policeman

483 District Nurse

484 Industrialist

47

Telephone Centenary

1976 (10 MAR.) 'All-over' phosphor ✓

997	**481**	8½p multicoloured ..	20	20	☐	☐
998	**482**	10p multicoloured ..	25	25	☐	☐
999	**483**	11p multicoloured ..	30	30	☐	☐
1000	**484**	13p multicoloured ..	35	35	☐	☐
		Set of 4	1·00	1·00	☐	☐
		First Day Cover		1·25		☐
		Presentation Pack ..	2·00		☐	
		Set of 4 Gutter Pairs ..	2·50		☐	
		Set of 4 Traffic Light Gutter Pairs	8·00		☐	

485 Hewing Coal
(Thomas Hepburn)

486 Machinery
(Robert Owen)

487 Chimney Cleaning
(Lord Shaftesbury)

488 Hands clutching Prison
Bars (Elizabeth Fry)

Social Reformers

1976 (28 APR.) 'All-over phosphor ✓

1001	**485**	8½p multicoloured ..	20	20	☐	☐
1002	**486**	10p multicoloured ..	25	25	☐	☐
1003	**487**	11p black, slate-grey and drab	30	30	☐	☐
1004	**488**	13p slate-grey, black and green	35	35	☐	☐
		Set of 4	1·00	1·00	☐	☐
		First Day Cover		1·25		☐
		Presentation Pack ..	2·00		☐	
		PHQ Card (No. 1001) ..	5·00	7·50	☐	☐
		Set of 4 Gutter Pairs ..	2·50		☐	
		Set of 4 Traffic Light Gutter Pairs	8·00		☐	

489 Benjamin Franklin (bust by
Jean-Jacques Caffieri)

Bicentenary of American Independence

1976 (2 JUNE) 'All-over' phosphor ✓

1005	**489**	11p multicoloured ..	50	50	☐	☐
		First Day Cover		1·00		☐
		Presentation Pack	1·25		☐	
		PHQ Card	2·50	8·50	☐	☐
		Gutter Pair	1·00		☐	
		Traffic Light Gutter Pair ..	3·00		☐	

490 'Elizabeth of Glamis'

491 'Grandpa Dickson'

492 'Rosa Mundi'

493 'Sweet Briar'

Centenary of Royal National Rose Society

1976 (30 JUNE) 'All-over' phosphor ✓

1006	**490**	8½p multicoloured ..	20	20	☐	☐
1007	**491**	10p multicoloured ..	30	30	☐	☐
1008	**492**	11p multicoloured ..	45	50	☐	☐
1009	**493**	13p multicoloured ..	45	40	☐	☐
		Set of 4	1·25	1·25	☐	☐
		First Day Cover		1·75		☐
		Presentation Pack ..	2·25		☐	
		PHQ Cards (set of 4) ..	30·00	14·00	☐	☐
		Set of 4 Gutter Pairs ..	2·50		☐	
		Set of 4 Traffic Light Gutter Pairs	10·00		☐	

494 Archdruid

495 Morris Dancing

496 Scots Piper   **497** Welsh Harpist

British Cultural Traditions

1976 (4 AUG.) *'All-over' phosphor*

1010	**494**	8½p multicoloured ..	20	20	☐	☐
1011	**495**	10p multiccloured ..	25	25	☐	☐
1012	**496**	11p multicoloured ..	30	30	☐	☐
1013	**497**	13p multicoloured ..	35	35	☐	☐
		Set of 4	1·00	1·00	☐	☐
		First Day Cover ..		1·25		☐
		Presentation Pack ..	2·00		☐	
		PHQ Cards (set of 4)	18·00	10·00	☐	☐
		Set of 4 Gutter Pairs	2·50		☐	
		Set of 4 Traffic Light Gutter Pairs ..	10·00		☐	

498 The Canterbury Tales   **499** The Tretyse of Love

500 Game and Playe of Chesse   **501** Early Printing Press

500th Anniversary of British Printing

1976 (29 SEPT.) *'All-over' phosphor*

1014	**498**	8½p blk, bl & gold	20	20	☐	☐
1015	**499**	10p blk, olive-grn & gold	25	25	☐	☐
1016	**500**	11p blk, grey & gold ..	30	30	☐	☐
1017	**501**	13p brn, ochre & gold ..	35	35	☐	☐
		Set of 4	1·00	1·00	☐	☐
		First Day Cover		1·25		☐
		Presentation Pack ..	2·50		☐	
		PHQ Cards (set of 4) ..	14·00	10·00	☐	☐
		Set of 4 Gutter Pairs	2·50		☐	
		Set of 4 Traffic Light Gutter Pairs	8·00		☐	

502 Virgin and Child   **503** Angel with Crown

504 Angel appearing to Shepherds   **505** The Three Kings

Christmas

1976 (24 Nov.) *Designs show English mediaeval embroidery. One phosphor band (6½p) or 'all-over' phosphor (others)*

1018	**502**	6½p multicoloured ..	15	15	☐	☐
1019	**503**	8½p multicoloured ..	20	20	☐	☐
1020	**504**	11p multicoloured ..	35	35	☐	☐
1021	**505**	13p multicoloured ..	40	40	☐	☐
		Set of 4	1·00	1·00	☐	☐
		First Day Cover ..		1·25		☐
		Presentation Pack ..	2·00		☐	
		PHQ Cards (set of 4) ..	4·00	8·00	☐	☐
		Set of 4 Gutter Pairs ..	2·50		☐	
		Set of 4 Traffic Light Gutter Pairs	8·00		☐	

Collectors Pack 1976

1976 (24 Nov.) *Comprises Nos. 997/1021*

Collectors Pack	10·00		☐

506 Lawn Tennis   **507** Table Tennis

508 Squash   **509** Badminton

Racket Sports

1977 (12 Jan.) *Phosphorised paper* ✓

1022	**506**	8½p multicoloured ..	20	20	☐ ☐
1023	**507**	10p multicoloured	25	25	☐ ☐
1024	**508**	11p multicoloured	30	30	☐ ☐
1025	**509**	13p multicoloured	35	35	☐ ☐
		Set of 4	1·00	1·00	☐ ☐
		First Day Cover ..		1·50	☐
		Presentation Pack ..	2·00		☐
		PHO Cards (set of 4)	6·00	9·50	☐ ☐
		Set of 4 Gutter Pairs ..	2·50		☐
		Set of 4 Traffic Light Gutter Pairs	8·00		☐

510

1977 (2 Feb.)–**87** *Type* **510** *Ordinary paper*

1026	£1 green and olive	3·00	20	☐ ☐
1026*b*	£1·30 drab & dp grnish bl ..	6·50	6·00	☐ ☐
1026*c*	£1·33 pale mve & grey-blk ..	6·50	6·00	☐ ☐
1026*d*	£1·41 drab & dp grnish bl ..	7·00	6·00	☐ ☐
1026*e*	£1·50 pale mve & grey-blk ..	6·00	4·00	☐ ☐
1026*f*	£1·60 drab and dp grnish bl	6·00	6·00	☐ ☐
1027	£2 green and brown ..	5·50	75	☐ ☐
1028	£5 pink and blue ..	13·00	2·00	☐ ☐
	Presentation Pack (Nos. 1026, 1027/8) ..	22·00		☐
	Presentation Pack (No. 1026*f*) ..	12·00		☐

First Day Covers

2 Feb.	1977	Nos: 1026, 1027/8	8·00	☐
3 Aug.	1983	No. 1026*b*	6·00	☐
28 Aug.	1984	No. 1026*c*	6·00	☐
17 Sept.	1985	No. 1026*d*	6·00	☐
2 Sept.	1986	No. 1026*e*	4·00	☐
15 Sept.	1987	No. 1026*f*	6·00	☐

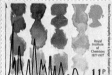

513 Starch – Chromatography

514 Salt – Crystallography

Centenary of Royal Institute of Chemistry

1977 (2 Mar.) *'All-over' phosphor* ✓

1029	**511**	8½p multicoloured ..	20	20	☐ ☐
1030	**512**	10p multicoloured ..	30	30	☐ ☐
1031	**513**	11p multicoloured ..	30	30	☐ ☐
1032	**514**	13p multicoloured ..	30	30	☐ ☐
		Set of 4	1·00	1·00	☐ ☐
		First Day Cover ..		1·40	☐
		Presentation Pack ..	2·40		☐
		PHO Cards (set of 4)	7·00	10·00	☐ ☐
		Set of 4 Gutter Pairs ..	2·50		☐
		Set of 4 Traffic Light Gutter Pairs	8·00		☐

515

Silver Jubilee

1977 (11 May–15 June) *'All-over' phosphor* ✓

1033	**515**	8½p multicoloured ..	20	20	☐ ☐
1034		9p mult (15 June) ..	25	25	☐ ☐
1035		10p multicoloured ..	25	25	☐ ☐
1036		11p multicoloured ..	30	30	☐ ☐
1037		13p multicoloured ..	40	40	☐ ☐
		Set of 5	1·25	1·25	☐ ☐
		First Day Covers (2)		1·50	☐
		Presentation Pack (ex 9p)	2·00		☐
		Souvenir Book (ex 9p) ..	4·00		☐
		PHO Cards (set of 5)	12·00	8·00	☐ ☐
		Set of 5 Gutter Pairs ..	2·75		☐
		Set of 5 Traffic Light Gutter Pairs	4·50		☐

511 Steroids – Conformational Analysis

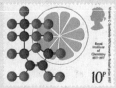

512 Vitamin C – Synthesis

519 'Gathering of Nations'

Commonwealth Heads of Government Meeting, London

1977 (8 JUNE) *'All-over' phosphor*

1038	**519**	13p black, deep green rose and silver ..		50	50	☐	☐
		First Day Cover	.. ..		1·00		☐
		Presentation Pack	.. ..	1·00		☐	
		PHQ Card	.. .. ..	2·25	3·75	☐	☐
		Gutter Pair	.. .. ..	1·00		☐	
		Traffic Light Gutter Pair		1·25		☐	

9ᵖ

9ᵖ

520 Hedgehog

521 Brown Hare

9ᵖ

9ᵖ

522 Red Squirrel

523 Otter

9ᵖ

T **520/4** were printed together, *se-tenant*, throughout the sheet

524 Badger

British Wildlife

1977 (5 OCT.) *'All-over' phosphor*

1039	**520**	9p multicoloured ..		25	20	☐	☐
		a. Strip of 5. Nos. 1039/43 ..		1·50	1·50	☐	☐
1040	**521**	9p multicoloured ..		25	20	☐	☐
1041	**522**	9p multicoloured ..		25	20	☐	☐
1042	**523**	9p multicoloured ..		25	20	☐	☐
1043	**524**	9p multicoloured ..		25	20	☐	☐
		Set of 5		1·50	90	☐	☐
		First Day Cover			2·25		☐
		Presentation Pack ..		2·25		☐	
		PHQ Cards (set of 5) ..		4·00	5·00	☐	☐
		Gutter Strip of 10		3·75		☐	
		Traffic Light Gutter Strip of 10		4·00		☐	

525 'Three French Hens, Two Turtle Doves and a Partridge in a Pear Tree'

526 'Six Geese a-laying, Five Gold Rings, Four Colly Birds'

527 'Eight Maids a-milking, Seven Swans a-swimming'

528 'Ten Pipers piping, Nine Drummers drumming'

529 'Twelve Lords a-leaping, Eleven Ladies dancing'

530 'A Partridge in a Pear Tree'

T **525/30** depict the carol 'The Twelve Days of Christmas'. T **525/29** were printed horizontally *se-tenant* throughout the sheet.

Christmas

1977 (23 Nov.) *One centre phosphor band (7p) or 'all-over' phosphor (9p)*

1044	**525**	7p multicoloured		15	15	☐	☐
		a. Strip of 5 Nos. 1044/8 ..		90	1·00	☐	☐
1045	**526**	7p multicoloured ..		15	15	☐	☐
1046	**527**	7p multicoloured ..		15	15	☐	☐
1047	**528**	7p multicoloured .		15	15	☐	☐
1048	**529**	7p multicoloured ..		15	15	☐	☐
1049	**530**	9p multicoloured ..		20	20	☐	☐
		Set of 6		1·00	85	☐	☐
		First Day Cover			1·40		☐
		Presentation Pack ..		2·00		☐	
		PHQ Cards (set of 6) ..		3·25	4·00	☐	☐
		Set of 6 Gutter Pairs		2·50		☐	
		Set of 6 Traffic Light Gutter Pairs		4·50		☐	

Collectors Pack 1977

1977 (23 Nov.) *Comprises Nos.* 1022/5. 1029/49

	Collectors Pack	.. ..		7·00	☐

531 Oil—North Sea Production Platform

532 Coal—Modern Pithead

533 Natural Gas—Flame Rising from Sea

534 Electricity—Nuclear Power Station and Uranium Atom

Energy Resources

1978 (25 Jan.) *'All-over' phosphor* ✔

1050	**531**	9p multicoloured ..	25	20	☐	☐
1051	**532**	10½p multicoloured ..	25	30	☐	☐
1052	**533**	11p multicoloured ..	30	30	☐	☐
1053	**534**	13p multicoloured ..	30	30	☐	☐
	Set of 4		1·00	1·00	☐	☐
	First Day Cover			1·25		☐
	Presentation Pack		2·00		☐	
	PHQ Cards (set of 4)		4·00	4·00	☐	☐
	Set of 4 Gutter Pairs ..		2·50		☐	
	Set of 4 Traffic Light Gutter Pairs		4·00		☐	

535 Tower of London

536 Holyroodhouse

537 Caernarvon Castle

538 Hampton Court Palace

British Architecture (Historic Buildings)

1978 (1 Mar.) *'All-over' phosphor* ✔

1054	**535**	9p multicoloured ..	25	20	☐	☐
1055	**536**	10½p multicoloured ..	25	30	☐	☐
1056	**537**	11p multicoloured ..	30	30	☐	☐
1057	**538**	13p multicoloured ..	30	30	☐	☐
	Set of 4		1·00	1·00	☐	☐
	First Day Cover			1·25		
	Presentation Pack		2·00		☐	
	PHQ Cards (set of 4) ..		4·00	5·00	☐	☐
	Set of 4 Gutter Pairs ..		2·50	-	☐	
	Set of 4 Traffic Light Gutter Pairs		4·00		☐	
MS1058	121×90 mm. Nos. 1054/57		1·25	1·50	☐	☐
	First Day Cover			2·00		☐

No. **MS**1058 was sold at 53½p, the premium being used for the London 1980 Stamp Exhibition.

539 State Coach

540 St Edward's Crown

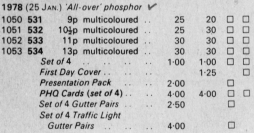

541 The Sovereign's Orb

542 Imperial State Crown

25th Anniversary of Coronation

1978 (31 May) *'All-over' phosphor* ✔

1059	**539**	9p gold and blue ..	20	20	☐	☐
1060	**540**	10½p gold and red ..	25	30	☐	☐
1061	**541**	11p gold and green ..	30	30	☐	☐
1062	**542**	13p gold and violet ..	35	30	☐	☐
	Set of 4		1·00	1·00	☐	☐
	First Day Cover			1·25		☐
	Presentation Pack		2·00		☐	
	Souvenir Book		4·00		☐	
	PHQ Cards (set of 4)		2·50	4·00	☐	☐
	Set of 4 Gutter Pairs ..		2·50		☐	
	Set of 4 Traffic Light Gutter Pairs		4·00		☐	

543 Shire Horse

544 Shetland Pony

545 Welsh Pony

546 Thoroughbred

Horses

1978 (5 July) *'All-over' phosphor*

1063	**543**	9p multicoloured ..	20	20	□	□
1064	**544**	10½p multicoloured ..	25	25	□	□
1065	**545**	11p multicoloured ..	30	30	□	□
1066	**546**	13p multicoloured ..	35	35	□	□
	Set of 4	1·00	1·00	□	□
	First Day Cover		1·50		□
	Presentation Pack	2·00		□
	PHQ Cards (set of 4) ..	2·50	6·00	□	□
	Set of 4 Gutter Pairs ..	2·50		□
	Set of 4 Traffic Light Gutter Pairs	4·00		□

547 Penny-farthing and 1884 Safety Bicycle

548 1920 Touring Bicycles

549 Modern Small-wheel Bicycles

550 1978 Road-racers

Centenaries of Cyclists Touring Club and British Cycling Federation

1978 (2 Aug.) *'All-over' phosphor*

1067	**547**	9p multicoloured ..	20	20	□	□
1068	**548**	10½p multicoloured ..	25	25	□	□
1069	**549**	11p multicoloured ..	30	30	□	□
1070	**550**	13p multicoloured ..	35	35	□	□
	Set of 4	1·00	1·00	□	□
	First Day Cover		1·25		□
	Presentation Pack	2·00		□
	PHQ Cards (set of 4) ..	1·50	3·25	□	□
	Set of 4 Gutter Pairs	2·50		□
	Set of 4 Traffic Light Gutter Pairs	4·00		□

551 Singing Carols round the Christmas Tree

552 The Waits

553 18th-Century Carol Singers

554 'The Boar's Head Carol'

Christmas

1978 (22 Nov.) One centre phosphor band (7p) or 'all-over' phosphor (others)

1071	**551**	7p multicoloured ..	20	20	□	□
1072	**552**	9p multicoloured ..	25	25	□	□
1073	**553**	11p multicoloured ..	30	30	□	□
1074	**554**	13p multicoloured ..	35	35	□	□
	Set of 4	1·00	1·00	□	□
	First Day Cover		1·25		□
	Presentation Pack	1·75		□
	PHQ Cards (set of 4) ..	1·50	4·00	□	□
	Set of 4 Gutter Pairs ..	2·50		□
	Set of 4 Traffic Light Gutter Pairs	3·00		□

Collectors Pack 1978

1978 (22 Nov.) *Comprises Nos.* 1050/7, 1059/74

	Collectors Pack	7·00		□

555 Old English Sheepdog

556 Welsh Springer Spaniel

557 West Highland Terrier   558 Irish Setter

Dogs

1979 (7 Feb.) *'All-over' phosphor*

1075	**555**	9p multicoloured		20	20	☐	☐
1076	**556**	10½p multicoloured		30	30	☐	☐
1077	**557**	11p multicoloured		30	30	☐	☐
1078	**558**	13p multicoloured		30	30	☐	☐
		Set of 4		1·00	1·00	☐	☐
		First Day Cover			1·50	☐	
		Presentation Pack		2·00		☐	
		PHQ Cards (set of 4)		3·00	5·00	☐	☐
		Set of 4 'Gutter Pairs		2·50		☐	
		Set of 4 Traffic Light					
		Gutter Pairs		3·75		☐	

559 Primrose

560 Daffodil

561 Bluebell

562 Snowdrop

Spring Wild Flowers

1979 (21 Mar.) *'All-over' phosphor*

1079	**559**	9p multicoloured		20	20	☐	☐
1080	**560**	10½p multicoloured		30	30	☐	☐
1081	**561**	11p multicoloured		30	30	☐	☐
1082	**562**	13p multicoloured		30	30	☐	☐
		Set of 4		1·00	1·00	☐	☐
		First Day Cover			1·50	☐	
		Presentation Pack		2·00		☐	
		PHQ Cards (set of 4)		2·00	4·00	☐	☐
		Set of 4 Gutter Pairs		2·50		☐	
		Set of 4 Traffic Light					
		Gutter Pairs		3·75		☐	

563

564

565

566

T **563/6** show hands placing the flags of the member nations into ballot boxes.

First Direct Elections to European Assembly

1979 (9 May) *Phosphorised paper*

1083	**563**	9p multicoloured		20	20	☐	☐
1084	**564**	10½p multicoloured		30	30	☐	☐
1085	**565**	11p multicoloured		30	30	☐	☐
1086	**566**	13p multicoloured		30	30	☐	☐
		Set of 4		1·00	1·00	☐	☐
		First Day Cover			1·25	☐	
		Presentation Pack		2·00		☐	
		PHQ Cards (set of 4)		1·50	3·50	☐	☐
		Set of 4 Gutter Pairs		2·50		☐	
		Set of 4 Traffic Light					
		Gutter Pairs		3·75		☐	

567 'Saddling "Mahmoud" for the Derby, 1936' (Sir Alfred Munnings)

568 'The Liverpool Great National Steeple Chase, 1839' (aquatint by F. C Turner)

569 'The First Spring Meeting, Newmarket, 1793' (J. N Sartorius)

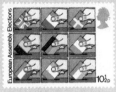

570 'Racing at Dorsett Ferry, Windsor, 1684' (Francis Barlow)

Horseracing Paintings and Bicentenary of The Derby (9p)

1979 (6 June) 'All-over' phosphor

1087	**567**	9p multicoloured	25	25	☐	☐
1088	**568**	10½p multicoloured	30	30	☐	☐
1089	**569**	11p multicoloured	30	30	☐	☐
1090	**570**	13p multicoloured	30	30	☐	☐
		Set of 4	1·10	1·10	☐	☐
		First Day Cover		1·50		☐
		Presentation Pack	2·00		☐	
		PHQ Cards (set of 4)	1·50	3·00	☐	☐
		Set of 4 Gutter Pairs	2·50		☐	
		Set of 4 Traffic Light				
		Gutter Pairs	3·75		☐	

571 The Tale of Peter Rabbit (Beatrix Potter)

572 The Wind in the Willows (Kenneth Grahame)

573 Winnie-the-Pooh (A. A. Milne)

574 Alice's Adventures in Wonderland (Lewis Carroll)

T **571/4** depict original illustrations from the four books.

International Year of the Child

1979 (11 July) 'All-over' phosphor

1091	**571**	9p multicoloured	35	20	☐	☐
1092	**572**	10½p multicoloured	40	35	☐	☐
1093	**573**	11p multicoloured	45	40	☐	☐
1094	**574**	13p multicoloured	50	55	☐	☐
		Set of 4	1·50	1·40	☐	☐
		First Day Cover		2·00		☐
		Presentation Pack	2·25		☐	
		PHQ Cards (set of 4)	2·50	3·00	☐	☐
		Set of 4 Gutter Pairs	4·00		☐	
		Set of 4 Traffic Light				
		Gutter Pairs	4·75		☐	

For full information on all future British issues, collectors should write to the British Post Office Philatelic Bureau, 20 Brandon Street, Edinburgh EH3 5TT

575 Sir Rowland Hill, 1795–1879

576 General Post, c. 1839

577 London Post, c. 1839

578 Uniform Postage, 1840

Death Centenary of Sir Rowland Hill (Postal Reformer)

1979 (22 Aug.–24 Oct.) 'All-over' phosphor

1095	**575**	10p multicoloured	25	25	☐	☐
1096	**576**	11½p multicoloured	30	35	☐	☐
1097	**577**	13p multicoloured	35	40	☐	☐
1098	**578**	15p multicoloured	50	40	☐	☐
		Set of 4	1·25	1·25	☐	☐
		First Day Cover		1·25		☐
		Presentation Pack	2·00		☐	
		PHQ Cards (set of 4)	1·50	3·00	☐	☐
		Set of 4 Gutter Pairs	2·50		☐	
		Set of 4 Traffic Light				
		Gutter Pairs	3·75		☐	
MS1099	89×121 mm. Nos. 1095/8		1·25	1·25	☐	☐
		First Day Cover (24 Oct.)		1·25		☐

No. **MS**1099 was sold at 59½p, the premium being used for the London 1980 Stamp Exhibition.

579 Policeman on the Beat

580 Policeman directing Traffic

13ᴾ

15ᴾ

581 Mounted Policewoman

582 River Patrol Boat

150th Anniversary of Metropolitan Police

1979 (26 SEPT.) *Phosphorised paper*

1100	**579**	10p multicoloured	..	25	25	☐	☐
1101	**580**	11½p multicoloured	..	30	35	☐	☐
1102	**581**	13p multicoloured	..	35	40	☐	☐
1103	**582**	15p multicoloured	..	50	40	☐	☐
		Set of 4	..	..	1·25	1·25	☐	☐
		First Day Cover	..	..		1·25		☐
		Presentation Pack	..	..	2·00		☐
		PHQ Cards (set of 4)	..	1·50	3·00	☐	☐
		Set of 4 Gutter Pairs	..	2·50		☐
		Set of 4 Traffic Light				
		Gutter Pairs	..	..	3·75		☐

8ᴾ

10ᴾ

583 The Three Kings

584 Angel appearing to the Shepherds

11½ᴾ

13ᴾ

585 The Nativity

586 Mary and Joseph travelling to Bethlehem

15ᴾ

587 The Annunciation

Christmas

1979 (21 Nov.) *One centre phosphor band (8p) or phosphorised paper (others)*

1104	**583**	8p multicoloured	..	20	20	☐	☐
1105	**584**	10p multicoloured	..	25	25	☐	☐
1106	**585**	11½p multicoloured	..	30	35	☐	☐
1107	**586**	13p multicoloured	..	40	40	☐	☐
1108	**587**	15p multicoloured	..	50	45	☐	☐
		Set of 5	..	..	1·50	1·50	☐	☐
		First Day Cover	..	..		1·50		☐
		Presentation Pack	..		2·25		☐
		PHQ Cards (set of 5)	..	1·50	3·50	☐	☐
		Set of 5 Gutter Pairs	..	3·00		☐
		Set of 5 Traffic Light				
		Gutter Pairs	..		3·75		☐

Collectors Pack 1979

1979 (21 Nov.) *Comprises Nos. 1075/98, 1100/8*

	Collectors Pack	..	..	9·00	☐

KINGFISHER 10ᴾ

DIPPER 11½ᴾ

588 Kingfisher

589 Dipper

MOORHEN 13ᴾ

YELLOW WAGTAIL 15ᴾ

590 Moorhen

591 Yellow Wagtails

Centenary of Wild Bird Protection Act

1980 (16 JAN.) *Phosphorised paper*

1109	**588**	10p multicoloured	..	25	25	☐	☐
1110	**589**	11½p multicoloured	..	30	35	☐	☐
1111	**590**	13p multicoloured	..	40	40	☐	☐
1112	**591**	15p multicoloured	..	45	45	☐	☐
		Set of 4	..	..	1·25	1·25	☐	☐
		First Day Cover	..	..		1·40		☐
		Presentation Pack	..	2·00		☐
		PHQ Cards (set of 4)	..	1·50	3·00	☐	☐
		Set of 4 Gutter Pairs	..	2·50		☐

592 *Rocket* approaching Moorish Arch, Liverpool

593 First and Second Class Carriages passing through Olive Mount Cutting

594 Third Class Carriage and Cattle Truck crossing Chat Moss

595 Horsebox and Carriage Truck near Bridgewater Canal

596 Goods Truck and Mail-coach at Manchester

T **592/6** were printed together, *se-tenant* in horizontal strips of 5 throughout the sheet.

150th Anniversary of Liverpool and Manchester Railway

1980 (12 MAR.) *Phosphorised paper*

1113	592	12p multicoloured ..	25	25	☐	☐
		a. *Strip of* 5.				
		Nos. 1113/17 ..	1·50	1·60	☐	☐
1114	593	12p multicoloured ..	25	25	☐	☐
1115	594	12p multicoloured ..	25	25	☐	☐
1116	595	12p multicoloured ..	25	25	☐	☐
1117	596	12p multicoloured ..	25	25	☐	☐
		Set of 5	1·50	1·10	☐	☐
		First Day Cover		1·60		☐
		Presentation Pack	2·50		☐	
		PHQ Cards (*set of* 5)	1·50	3·75	☐	☐
		Gutter strip of 10	3·25		☐	

> **Minimum Price**. The minimum price quoted is 10p. This represents a handling charge rather than a basis for valuing common stamps. Where the actual value of a stamp is less than 10p this may be apparent when set prices are shown, particularly for sets including a number of 10p stamps. It therefore follows that in valuing common stamps the 10p catalogue price should not be reckoned automatically since it covers a variation in real scarcity.

597 Montage of London Buildings

"London 1980" International Stamp Exhibition

1980 (9 APR–7 MAY) *Phosphorised paper. Perf* $14\frac{1}{2} \times 14$

1118	597	50p agate	1·50	1·50	☐	☐
		First Day Cover		1·50		☐
		Presentation Pack	2·00		☐	
		PHQ Card	50	1·75	☐	☐
		Gutter Pair	3·00		☐	
MS1119		90 × 123 mm. No. 1118	1·50	1·50	☐	☐
		First Day Cover (7 May)		1·50		☐

No. **MS**1119 was sold at 75p, the premium being used for the exhibition.

598 Buckingham Palace

599 The Albert Memorial

600 Royal Opera House

601 Hampton Court

57

17½p Kensington Palace

602 Kensington Palace

HER MAJESTY QUEEN ELIZABETH THE QUEEN MOTHER 80TH BIRTHDAY 12p

607 Queen Elizabeth the Queen Mother

London Landmarks

1980 (7 MAY) *Phosphorised paper*

1120	**598**	10½p multicoloured ..	25	25	☐	☐
1121	**599**	12p multicoloured ..	30	30	☐	☐
1122	**600**	13½p multicoloured ..	35	35	☐	☐
1123	**601**	15p multicoloured ..	40	40	☐	☐
1124	**602**	17½p multicoloured ..	40	40	☐	☐
		Set of 5	1·50	1·50	☐	☐
		First Day Cover		1·75		☐
		Presentation Pack	2·50		☐	
		PHQ Cards (set of 5) ..	1·50	3·00	☐	☐
		Set of 5 Gutter Pairs	3·00		☐	

12p Charlotte Brontë: Jane Eyre

13½p George Eliot: The Mill on the Floss

603 Charlotte Bronte
(*Jane Eyre*)

604 George Eliot (*The Mill on the Floss*)

15p Emily Brontë: Wuthering Heights

17½p Mrs Gaskell: North and South

605 Emily Bronte
(*Wuthering Heights*)

606 Mrs Gaskell (*North and South*)

T **603/6** show authoresses and scenes from their novels. T **603/4** also include the "Europa" C.E.P.T. emblem.

Famous Authoresses

1980 (9 JULY) *Phosphorised paper*

1125	**603**	12p multicoloured ..	30	30	☐	☐
1126	**604**	13½p multicoloured ..	35	35	☐	☐
1127	**605**	15p multicoloured ..	40	45	☐	☐
1128	**606**	17½p multicoloured ..	60	60	☐	☐
		Set of 4	1·50	1·50	☐	☐
		First Day Cover		1·50		☐
		Presentation Pack	2·50		☐	
		PHQ Cards (set of 4) ..	1·50	3·00	☐	☐
		Set of 4 Gutter Pairs	3·00		☐	

80th Birthday of Queen Elizabeth the Queen Mother

1980 (4 AUG.) *Phosphorised paper*

1129	**607**	12p multicoloured ..	50	50	☐	☐
		First Day Cover		60		☐
		PHQ Card	50	1·25	☐	☐
		Gutter Pair	1·00		☐	

12p Sir Henry Wood

13½p Sir Thomas Beecham

608 Sir Henry Wood

609 Sir Thomas Beecham

15p Sir Malcolm Sargent

17½p Sir John Barbirolli

610 Sir Malcolm Sargent

611 Sir John Barbirolli

British Conductors

1980 (10 SEPT.) *Phosphorised paper*

1130	**608**	12p multicoloured ..	30	30	☐	☐
1131	**609**	13½p multicoloured ..	35	40	☐	☐
1132	**610**	15p multicoloured ..	45	45	☐	☐
1133	**611**	17½p multicoloured ..	55	50	☐	☐
		Set of 4	1·50	1·50	☐	☐
		First Day Cover		1·50		☐
		Presentation Pack	2·00		☐	
		PHQ Cards (set of 4) ..	1·50	2·50	☐	☐
		Set of 4 Gutter Pairs	3·00		☐	

612 Running

613 Rugby

614 Boxing

615 Cricket

Sports Centenaries

1980 (10 Oct.) *Phosphorised paper. Perf 14 × 14½*

1134	**612**	12p multicoloured ..	30	30	☐	☐
1135	**613**	13½p multicoloured ..	35	40	☐	☐
1136	**614**	15p multicoloured ..	40	40	☐	☐
1137	**615**	17½p multicoloured ..	60	55	☐	☐
		Set of 4	1·50	1·50	☐	☐
		First Day Cover		1·50		☐
		Presentation Pack	2·00		☐	
		PHQ Cards (set of 4) ..	1·50	2·50	☐	☐
		Set of 4 Gutter Pairs	3·00		☐	

Centenaries:– 12p Amateur Athletics Association; 13½p Welsh Rugby Union; 15p Amateur Boxing Association; 17½p First England v Australia Test Match.

618 Apples and Mistletoe

619 Crown, Chains and Bell

620 Holly

Christmas

1980 (19 Nov.) *One centre phosphor band (10p) or phosphorised paper (others)*

1138	**616**	10p multicoloured ..	25	25	☐	☐
1139	**617**	12p multicoloured ..	30	35	☐	☐
1140	**618**	13½p multicoloured ..	35	40	☐	☐
1141	**619**	15p multicoloured ..	40	40	☐	☐
1142	**620**	17½p multicoloured ..	40	40	☐	☐
		Set of 5	1·50	1·60	☐	☐
		First Day Cover		1·60		☐
		Presentation Pack	2·25		☐	
		PHQ Cards (set of 5) ..	1·50	2·50	☐	☐
		Set of 5 Gutter Pairs ..	3·00		☐	

Collectors Pack 1980

1980 (19 Nov.) *Comprises Nos.* 1109/18, 1120/42

	Collectors Pack	12·00	☐

616 Christmas Tree

617 Candles

621 St. Valentine's Day

622 Morris Dancers

623 Lammastide

624 Medieval Mummers

629 *Aglais urticae*

630 *Maculinea arion*

T **621/22** also include the "Europa" C.E.P.T. emblem.

Folklore

1981 (6 FEB.) *Phosphorised paper*

1143	**621**	14p multicoloured ..	35	35	☐	☐
1144	**622**	18p multicoloured ..	45	50	☐	☐
1145	**623**	22p multicoloured ..	60	60	☐	☐
1146	**624**	25p multicoloured ..	75	70	☐	☐
		Set of 4	2·00	2·00	☐	☐
		First Day Cover		2·00		☐
		Presentation Pack	2·50		☐	
		PHQ Cards (set of 4) ..	1·50	2·50	☐	☐
		Set of 4 Gutter Pairs ..	4·00		☐	

629 *Aglais urticae*

632 *Carterocephalus palaemon*

631 *Inachis io*

625 Blind Man with Guide Dog

626 Hands spelling "Deaf" in Sign Language

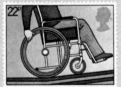

627 Disabled Man in Wheelchair

628 Disabled Artist painting with Foot

Butterflies

1981 (13 MAY) *Phosphorised paper*

1151	**629**	14p multicoloured ..	35	35	☐	☐
1152	**630**	18p multicoloured ..	50	50	☐	☐
1153	**631**	22p multicoloured ..	60	65	☐	☐
1154	**632**	25p multicoloured ..	70	75	☐	☐
		Set of 4	2·00	2·00	☐	☐
		First Day Cover		2·00		☐
		Presentation Pack	2·50		☐	
		PHQ Cards (set of 4) ..	2·00	3·00	☐	☐
		Set of 4 Gutter Pairs ..	4·00		☐	

633 Glenfinnan, Scotland

634 Derwentwater, England

International Year of the Disabled

1981 (25 MAR.) *Phosphorised paper*

1147	**625**	14p multicoloured ..	35	35	☐	☐
1148	**626**	18p multicoloured ..	45	50	☐	☐
1149	**627**	22p multicoloured ..	60	60	☐	☐
1150	**628**	25p multicoloured ..	75	70	☐	☐
		Set of 4	2·00	2·00	☐	☐
		First Day Cover		2·00		☐
		Presentation Pack	2·50		☐	
		PHQ Cards (set of 4) ..	1·50	2·75	☐	☐
		Set of 4 Gutter Pairs ..	4·00		☐	

635 Stackpole Head, Wales

636 Giant's Causeway, N. Ireland

637 St Kilda, Scotland

50th Anniversary of National Trust for Scotland

1981 (24 JUNE) *Phosphorised paper*

1155	**633**	14p multicoloured ..	30	30	☐	☐
1156	**634**	18p multicoloured ..	40	40	☐	☐
1157	**635**	20p multicoloured ..	50	50	☐	☐
1158	**636**	22p multicoloured ..	60	60	☐	☐
1159	**637**	25p multicoloured ..	70	70	☐	☐
		Set of 5	2·25	2·25	☐	☐
		First Day Cover..		2·25		☐
		Presentation Pack	2·75		☐	
		PHQ Cards (set of 5)	2·00	2·75	☐	☐
		Set of 5 Gutter Pairs	4·50		☐	

638 Prince Charles and Lady Diana Spencer

Royal Wedding

1981 (22 JULY) *Phosphorised paper*

1160	**638**	14p multicoloured ..	25	25	☐	☐
1161		25p multicoloured ..	75	75	☐	☐
		Set of 2	1·00	1·00	☐	☐
		First Day Cover		2·00		☐
		Presentation Pack	2·00		☐	
		Souvenir Book	4·00		☐	
		PHQ Cards (set of 2)	1·00	2·75	☐	☐
		Set of 2 Gutter Pairs	2·00		☐	

639 "Expeditions"

640 "Skills"

641 "Service"

642 "Recreation"

25th Anniversary of Duke of Edinburgh Award Scheme

1981 (12 AUG.) *Phosphorised paper. Perf* 14

1162	**639**	14p multicoloured ..	35	35	☐	☐
1163	**640**	18p multicoloured ..	50	50	☐	☐
1164	**641**	22p multicoloured ..	60	60	☐	☐
1165	**642**	25p multicoloured ..	70	70	☐	☐
		Set of 4	2·00	2·00	☐	☐
		First Day Cover..		2·00		☐
		Presentation Pack	2·50		☐	
		PHQ Cards (set of 4)	1·60	2·25	☐	☐
		Set of 4 Gutter Pairs ..	4·00		☐	

643 Cockle-Dredging from *Linsey II*

644 Hauling Trawl Net

645 Lobster Potting

646 Hoisting Seine Net

Fishing Industry

1981 (23 SEPT.) *Phosphorised paper*

1166	**643**	14p multicoloured ..	35	35	☐	☐
1167	**644**	18p multicoloured ..	50	50	☐	☐
1168	**645**	22p multicoloured ..	60	60	☐	☐
1169	**646**	25p multicoloured ..	70	65	☐	☐
		Set of 4	2·00	2·00	☐	☐
		First Day Cover..		2·00		☐
		Presentation Pack	2·50		☐	
		PHQ Cards (set of 4) ..	2·00	2·50	☐	☐
		Set of 4 Gutter Pairs ..	4·00		☐	

Nos. 1166/9 were issued on the occasion of the centenary of Royal National Mission to Deep Sea Fishermen.

647 Father Christmas

648 Jesus Christ

649 Flying Angel

650 Joseph and Mary arriving at Bethlehem

651 Three Kings approaching Bethlehem

Christmas. Children's Pictures

1981 (18 Nov.) *One phosphor band (11½p) or phosphorised paper (others)*

1170	**647**	11½p multicoloured	..	30	30	☐ ☐
1171	**648**	14p multicoloured	..	40	40	☐ ☐
1172	**649**	18p multicoloured	..	50	50	☐ ☐
1173	**650**	22p multicoloured	..	60	60	☐ ☐
1174	**651**	25p multicoloured	..	70	70	☐ ☐
		Set of 5	.. .. ..	2·25	2·25	☐
		First Day Cover	.. ..		2·25	☐
		Presentation Pack	.. ..	2·75		☐
		PHO Cards (set of 5)	.. ..	2·00	3·50	☐ ☐
		Set of 5 Gutter Pairs	.. ..	4·50		☐

Collectors Pack 1981

1981 (18 Nov.) *Comprises Nos. 1143/74*

Collectors Pack	.. .. .. 18·00	☐

For full information on all future British issues, collectors should write to the British Post Office Philatelic Bureau, 20 Brandon Street, Edinburgh EH3 5TT.

652 Charles Darwin and Giant Tortoises

653 Darwin and Marine Iguanas

654 Darwin, Cactus Ground Finch and Large Ground Finch

655 Darwin and Prehistoric Skulls

Death Centenary of Charles Darwin

1982 (10 Feb.) *Phosphorised paper*

1175	**652**	15½p multicoloured	..	35	35 ☐ ☐
1176	**653**	19½p multicoloured		60	60 ☐ ☐
1177	**654**	26p multicoloured		70	70 ☐ ☐
1178	**655**	29p multicoloured		75	75 ☐ ☐
		Set of 4	.. .. ..	2·25	2·25 ☐ ☐
		First Day Cover	.. ..		2·25 ☐
		Presentation Pack	..	3·00	☐
		PHQ Cards (set of 4)	..	2·50	6·50 ☐ ☐
		Set of 4 Gutter Pairs	..	4·50	☐

656 Boys' Brigade

657 Girls' Brigade

658 Boy Scout Movement

659 Girl Guide Movement

Youth Organizations

1982 (24 Mar.) *Phosphorised paper*

1179	**656**	15½p multicoloured	..	35	35	☐	☐
1180	**657**	19½p multicoloured	..	60	50	☐	☐
1181	**658**	26p multicoloured	..	85	75	☐	☐
1182	**659**	29p multicoloured	..	1·00	90	☐	☐
		Set of 4	.. .. ..	2·50	2·25	☐	☐
		First Day Cover	.. ..		2·25	☐	
		Presentation Pack	.∴ ..	3·50		☐	
		PHQ Cards (set of 4)	..	2·50	6·50	☐	☐
		Set of 4 Gutter Pairs	..	5·00		☐	

Nos. 1179/82 were issued on the occasion of the 75th anniversary of the Boy Scout Movement, the 125th birth anniversary of Lord Baden-Powell and the centenary of the Boys' Brigade (1983).

660 Ballerina

661 Harlequin

662 Hamlet

663 Opera Singer

Europa. British Theatre

1982 (28 Apr.) *Phosphorised paper*

1183	**660**	15½p multicoloured	..	35	35	☐	☐
1184	**661**	19½p multicoloured	..	60	50	☐	☐
1185	**662**	26p multicoloured	..	90	75	☐	☐
1186	**663**	29p multicoloured	..	1·25	90	☐	☐
		Set of 4	.. .. ..	2·75	2·25	☐	☐
		First Day Cover	.. ..		2·25	☐	
		Presentation Pack	..	3·25		☐	
		PHQ Cards (set of 4)	..	2·50	6·50	☐	☐
		Set of 4 Gutter Pairs	..	5·50		☐	

664 Henry VIII and *Mary Rose*

665 Admiral Blake and *Triumph*

666 Lord Nelson and HMS *Victory*

667 Lord Fisher and HMS *Dreadnought*

668 Viscount Cunningham and HMS *Warspite*

Maritime Heritage

1982 (16 June) *Phosphorised paper*

1187	**664**	15½p multicoloured	..	35	35	☐	☐
1188	**665**	19½p multicoloured	..	60	60	☐	☐
1189	**666**	24p multicoloured	..	70	70	☐	☐
1190	**667**	26p multicoloured	..	80	80	☐	☐
1191	**668**	29p multicoloured	..	90	90	☐	☐
		Set of 5	.. ..	3·00	3·00	☐	☐
		First Day Cover	.. ..		3·00	☐	
		Presentation Pack	..	3·50		☐	
		PHQ Cards (set of 5)	..	3·00	6·50	☐	☐
		Set of 5 Gutter Pairs	..	6·00		☐	

669 "Strawberry Thief" (William Morris)

670 Untitled (Steiner and Co)

671 "Cherry Orchard"
   (Paul Nash)

672 "Chevron" (Andrew
   Foster)

675 Austin "Seven" and "Metro"   676 Ford "Model T" and "Escort"

British Textiles

1982 (23 JULY) *Phosphorised paper*

1192	**669**	15½p multicoloured ..	35	35	☐	☐
1193	**670**	19½p multicoloured ..	55	55	☐	☐
1194	**671**	26p multicoloured ..	70	70	☐	☐
1195	**672**	29p multicoloured ..	90	90	☐	☐
		Set of 4	2·25	2·25	☐	☐
		First Day Cover		2·50		☐
		Presentation Pack	3·25		☐	
		PHQ Cards (*set of 4*)	3·00	6·50	☐	☐
		Set of 4 Gutter Pairs	4·50		☐	

Nos 1192/5 were issued on the occasion of the 250th birth anniversary of Sir Richard Arkwright (inventor of spinning machine).

677 Jaguar "SS1" and "XJ6"   678 Rolls-Royce "Silver Ghost"
                                 and "Silver Spirit"

British Motor Industry

1982 (13 OCT.) *Phosphorised paper*. Perf 14½ × 14

1198	**675**	15½p multicoloured ..	50	50	☐	☐
1199	**676**	19½p multicoloured ..	70	70	☐	☐
1200	**677**	26p multicoloured ..	85	90	☐	☐
1201	**678**	29p multicoloured ..	1·00	1·25	☐	☐
		Set of 4	2·75	3·00		☐
		First Day Cover		3·00		☐
		Presentation Pack	3·75		☐	
		PHQ Cards (*set of 4*)	3·00	7·00	☐	☐
		Set of 4 Gutter Pairs	5·50		☐	

673 Development of Communications

674 Modern Technological Aids

679 "While Shepherds Watched"   680 "The Holly and the Ivy"

Information Technology

1982 (8 SEPT.) *Phosphorised paper*. Perf 14 × 15

1196	**673**	15½p multicoloured ..	45	50	☐	☐
1197	**674**	26p multicoloured ..	80	85	☐	☐
		Set of 2	1·25	1·25	☐	☐
		First Day Cover		1·50		☐
		Presentation Pack	2·00		☐	
		PHQ Cards (*set of 2*)	1·50	4·50	☐	☐
		Set of 2 Gutter Pairs	2·50		☐	

681 "I Saw Three Ships"   682 "We Three Kings"

683 "Good King Wenceslas"

Christmas. Carols

1982 (17 Nov) *One phosphor band (12½p) or phosphorised paper (others)*

1202	**679**	12½p multicoloured	..	30	30	☐ ☐
1203	**680**	15½p multicoloured	..	40	40	☐ ☐
1204	**681**	19½p multicoloured	..	60	60	☐ ☐
1205	**682**	26p multicoloured	..	70	70	☐ ☐
1206	**683**	29p multicoloured	..	80	80	☐ ☐
		Set of 5	.. ..	2·50	2·50	☐ ☐
		First Day Cover	.. ..		2·50	☐
		Presentation Pack	..	3·00		☐
		PHQ Cards (set of 5)	..	3·00	7·00	☐ ☐
		Set of 5 Gutter Pairs	..	5·00		☐

Collectors Pack 1982

1982 (17 Nov.) *Comprises Nos.* 1175/1206

Collectors Pack	.. 24·00	☐

684 Salmon

685 Pike

686 Trout

687 Perch

British River Fishes

1983 (26 Jan.) *Phosphorised paper*

1207	**684**	15½p multicoloured	..	35	35	☐ ☐
1208	**685**	19½p multicoloured	..	55	55	☐ ☐
1209	**686**	26p multicoloured	..	70	70	☐ ☐
1210	**687**	29p multicoloured	..	90	90	☐ ☐
		Set of 4	.. ..	2·25	2·25	☐ ☐
		First Day Cover	.. ..		2·50	☐
		Presentation Pack	..	3·00		☐
		PHQ Cards (set of 4)	..	3·00	6·50	☐ ☐
		Set of 4 Gutter Pairs	..	4·50		☐

688 Tropical Island

689 Desert

690 Temperate Farmland

691 Mountain Range

Commonwealth Day. Geographical Regions

1983 (9 Mar.) *Phosphorised paper*

1211	**688**	15½p multicoloured	..	35	35	☐ ☐
1212	**689**	19½p multicoloured	..	55	55	☐ ☐
1213	**690**	26p multicoloured	..	70	70	☐ ☐
1214	**691**	29p multicoloured	..	90	90	☐ ☐
		Set of 4	.. ..	2·25	2·25	☐ ☐
		First Day Cover	.. ..		2·50	☐
		Presentation Pack	..	3·25		☐
		PHQ Cards (set of 4)	..	3·00	6·50	☐ ☐
		Set of 4 Gutter Pairs	..	4·50		☐

692 Humber Bridge

693 Thames Flood Barrier

694 *Iolair* (oilfield emergency support vessel)

Europa. Engineering Achievements

1983 (25 MAY) *Phosphorised paper.*

1215	**692**	16p multicoloured ..	45	45	☐	☐
1216	**693**	20½p multicoloured	95	1·10	☐	☐
1217	**694**	28p multicoloured	1·10	1·25	☐	☐
		Set of 3	2·25	2·50	☐	☐
		First Day Cover		2·75		☐
		Presentation Pack ..	3·50		☐	
		PHQ Cards (set of 3) ..	2·50	6·00	☐	☐
		Set of 3 Gutter Pairs	4·50		☐	

British Army Uniforms

1983 (6 JULY) *Phosphorised paper.*

1218	**695**	16p multicoloured ..	40	40	☐	☐
1219	**696**	20½p multicoloured	70	70	☐	☐
1220	**697**	26p multicoloured	85	85	☐	☐
1221	**698**	28p multicoloured	85	85	☐	☐
1222	**699**	31p multicoloured ..	1·10	1·10	☐	☐
		Set of 5	3·50	3·50	☐	☐
		First Day Cover		3·25		☐
		Presentation Pack ..	4·25		☐	
		PHQ Cards (set of 5) ..	3·00	6·00	☐	☐
		Set of 5 Gutter Pairs ..	7·00		☐	

Nos. 1218/22 were issued on the occasion of the 350th anniversary of The Royal Scots, the senior line regiment of the British Army.

695 Musketeer and Pikeman. The Royal Scots (1633)

696 Fusilier and Ensign. The Royal Welch Fusiliers (mid-18th century)

700 20th-Century Garden, Sissinghurst

701 19th-Century Garden, Biddulph Grange

697 Riflemen. 96th Rifles (The Royal Green Jackets) (1805)

698 Sergeant (khaki service uniform) and Guardsman (full dress). The Irish Guards (1900)

702 18th-Century Garden, Blenheim

703 17th-Century Garden, Pitmedden

699 Paratroopers. The Parachute Regiment (1983)

British Gardens

1983 (24 AUG) *Phosphorised paper. Perf 14*

1223	**700**	16p multicoloured ..	40	40	☐	☐
1224	**701**	20½p multicoloured ..	50	50	☐	☐
1225	**702**	28p multicoloured ..	70	90	☐	☐
1226	**703**	31p multicoloured ..	90	1·00	☐	☐
		Set of 4	2·25	2·50	☐	☐
		First Day Cover		2·75		☐
		Presentation Pack ..	3·50		☐	
		PHQ Cards (set of 4) ..	3·00	6·00	☐	☐
		Set of 4 Gutter Pairs	4·50		☐	

704 Merry-go-round

705 Big Wheel, Helter-skelter and Performing Animals

706 Side-shows

707 Early Produce Fair

British Fairs

1983 (5 Oct.) *Phosphorised paper.*

1227	**704**	16p multicoloured	..	40	40	□	□
1228	**705**	20½p multicoloured	..	65	65	□	□
1229	**706**	28p multicoloured	..	85	85	□	□
1230	**707**	31p multicoloured	..	90	90	□	□
	Set of 4	.. .. ..		2·50	2·50	□	□
	First Day Cover	.. .. ..			2·75		□
	Presentation Pack	.. ..		3·50		□	
	PHQ Cards (set of 4)	.. ..		3·00	6·00	□	□
	Set of 4 Gutter Pairs	..		5·00		□	

Nos. 1227/30 were issued to mark the 850th Anniversary of St. Bartholomew's Fair, Smithfield, London.

708 "Christmas Post" (pillar-box)

709 "The Three Kings" (chimney-pots)

710 "World at Peace" (Dove and Blackbird)

711 "Light of Christmas" (street lamp)

712 "Christmas Dove" (hedge sculpture)

Christmas

1983 (16 Nov.) *One phosphor band (12½p) or phosphorised paper (others)*

1231	**708**	12½p multicoloured	..	30	30	□	□
1232	**709**	16p multicoloured	..	35	35	□	□
1233	**710**	20½p multicoloured	..	60	60	□	□
1234	**711**	28p multicoloured	..	70	70	□	□
1235	**712**	31p multicoloured	..	85	1·00	□	□
	Set of 5	.. .. ..		2·50	2·75	□	□
	First Day Cover	.. .. ..			2·75		□
	Presentation Pack	.. .. ..		3·50		□	
	PHQ Cards (set of 5)	.. ..		3·00	6·00	□	□
	Set of 5 Gutter Pairs			5·00		□	

Collectors Pack 1983

1983 (16 Nov.) Comprises Nos. 1207/35

	Collectors Pack	.. ..	40·00	□

713 Arms of the College of Arms

714 Arms of King Richard III (founder)

715 Arms of the Earl Marshal of England

716 Arms of the City of London

67

500th Anniversary of College of Arms

1984 (17 Jan) *Phosphorised paper. Perf 14½*

1236	**713**	16p multicoloured		40	40	□ □
1237	**714**	20½p multicoloured		60	60	□ □
1238	**715**	28p multicoloured		85	85	□ □
1239	**716**	31p multicoloured		95	95	□ □
		Set of 4	..	2·50	2·50	□ □
		First Day Cover	..		2·50	□
		Presentation Pack		3·50		□
		PHQ Cards (set of 4)	..	3·00	6·00	□ □
		Set of 4 Gutter Pairs	..	5·00		□

717 Highland Cow

718 Chillingham Wild Bull

719 Hereford Bull

720 Welsh Black Bull

721 Irish Moiled Cow

British Cattle

1984 (6 Mar) *Phosphorised paper.*

1240	**717**	16p multicoloured	..	40	40	□ □
1241	**718**	20½p multicoloured	..	65	65	□ □
1242	**719**	26p multicoloured	..	70	70	□ □
1243	**720**	28p multicoloured	..	70	70	□ □
1244	**721**	31p multicoloured	..	90	90	□ □
		Set of 5	.. ..	3·00	3·00	□ □
		First Day Cover	.. ..		3·00	□
		Presentation Pack	.. ..	4·25		□
		PHQ Cards (set of 5)	.. ..	3·00	6·00	□ □
		Set of 5 Gutter Pairs	.. ..	6·00		□

Nos. 1240/4 marked the centenary of the Highland Cattle Society and the bicentenary of the Royal Highland and Agricultural Society of Scotland.

722 Festival Hall, Liverpool   **723** Milburngate Shopping Centre, Durham

724 Bush House, Bristol   **725** Commercial Street Housing Scheme, Perth

Urban Renewal

1984 (10 Apr) *Phosphorised paper.*

1245	**722**	16p multicoloured	..	40	40	□ □
1246	**723**	20½p multicoloured	..	60	60	□ □
1247	**724**	28p multicoloured	..	90	90	□ □
1248	**725**	31p multicoloured	..	90	90	□ □
		Set of 4	.. ..	2·50	2·50	□ □
		First Day Cover			3·00	□
		Presentation Pack	..	3·50		□
		PHQ Cards (set of 4)	..	3·00	6·00	□ □
		Set of 4 Gutter Pairs	..	5·00		□

Nos. 1245/8 mark the opening of the International Gardens Festival, Liverpool, and the 150th anniversaries of the Royal Institute of British Architects and the Chartered Institute of Building.

726 C.E.P.T. 25th Anniversary Logo   **727** Abduction of Europa

Nos. 1249/50 and 1251/2 were each printed together, *se-tenant*, in horizontal pairs throughout the sheets.

Europa. 25th Anniversary of C.E.P.T. and 2nd European Parliamentary Elections

1984 (15 May) *Phosphorised paper.*

1249	**726**	16p greenish slate, dp blue and gold ..	90	90	☐	☐
		a. *Horiz pair. Nos. 1249/50* ..	1·75	1·75	☐	☐
1250	**727**	16p greenish slate, dp bl, blk and gold ..	90	90	☐	☐
1251	**726**	20½p Venetian red, deep magenta and gold ..	1·50	1·50	☐	☐
		a. *Horizontal pair. Nos. 1251/2*	3·00	3·00	☐	☐
1252	**727**	.20½p Venetian red, deep magenta, black and gold ..	1·50	1·50	☐	☐
	Set of 4		4·25	4·25	☐	☐
	First Day Cover ..			4·25		☐
	Presentation Pack		5·00		☐	
	PHQ Cards (set of 4) ..		3·00	6·00	☐	☐
	Set of 4 Gutter Pairs ..		8·50		☐	

728 Lancaster House

London Economic Summit Conference

1984 (5 June) *Phosphorised paper.*

1253	**728**	31p multicoloured ..	1·00	1·00	☐	☐
	First Day Cover			2·00		☐
	PHQ Card		1·00	2·75	☐	☐
	Gutter Pair		2·00		☐	

729 View of Earth from "Apollo 11"

730 Navigational Chart of English Channel

731 Greenwich Observatory

732 Sir George Airey's Transit Telescope

Centenary of Greenwich Meridian

1984 (26 June) *Phosphorised paper. Perf 14 × 14½*

1254	**729**	16p multicoloured ..	40	40	☐	☐
1255	**730**	20½p multicoloured	65	65	☐	☐
1256	**731**	28p multicoloured ..	85	90	☐	☐
1257	**732**	31p multicoloured ..	90	1·10	☐	☐
	Set of 4		2·50	2·75	☐	☐
	First Day Cover			2·75		☐
	Presentation Pack		3·75		☐	
	PHQ Cards (set of 4) ..		3·00	6·00	☐	☐
	Set of 4 Gutter Pairs ..		5·00		☐	

733 Bath Mail Coach, 1784

734 Attack on Exeter Mail, 1816

735 Norwich Mail in Thunderstorm, 1827

736 Holyhead and Liverpool Mails leaving London, 1828

737 Edinburgh Mail Snowbound, 1831

T **733/7** were printed together, *se-tenant* in horizontal strips of 5 throughout the sheet.

Bicentenary of First Mail Coach Run, Bath and Bristol to London

1984 (31 JULY) *Phosphorised paper*

1258	**733**	16p multicoloured		60	60	☐	☐
		a. Horiz strip of 5.					
		Nos. 1258/62	..	2·75	2·75	☐	☐
1259	**734**	16p multicoloured	..	60	60	☐	☐
1260	**735**	16p multicoloured	..	60	60	☐	☐
1261	**736**	16p multicoloured	..	60	60	☐	☐
1262	**737**	16p multicoloured	..	60	60	☐	☐
		Set of 5	.. ..	2·75	2·75	☐	☐
		First Day Cover	.. ..		2·75		☐
		Presentation Pack ..	..	3·75		☐	
		Souvenir Book	..	6·00		☐	
		PHQ Cards (set of 5)	..	3·00	6·50	☐	☐
		Gutter Strip of 10 ..	.. ..	5·50		☐	

738 Nigerian Clinic

739 Violinist and Acropolis. Athens

740 Building Project, Sri Lanka

741 British Council Library

50th Anniversary of The British Council

1984 (25 SEPT.) *Phosphorised paper*

1263	**738**	17p multicoloured	..	50	50	☐	☐
1264	**739**	22p multicoloured	..	65	65	☐	☐
1265	**740**	31p multicoloured	..	90	90	☐	☐
1266	**741**	34p multicoloured	..	1·00	1·00	☐	☐
		Set of 4	.. ..	2·75	2·75	☐	☐
		First Day Cover	.. ..		2·75		☐
		Presentation Pack ..		3·50		☐	
		PHQ Cards (set of 4)	..	3·00	6·00	☐	☐
		Set of 4 Gutter Pairs	..	5·50		☐	

For full information on all future British issues, collectors should write to the British Post Office Philatelic Bureau, 20 Brandon Street, Edinburgh EH3 5TT.

742 The Holy Family

743 Arrival in Bethlehem

744 Shepherd and Lamb

745 Virgin and Child

746 Offering of Frankincense

Christmas

1984 (20 Nov) *One phosphor band (13p) or phosphorised paper (others)*

1267	**742**	13p multicoloured	..	30	30	☐	☐
1268	**743**	17p multicoloured	..	50	50	☐	☐
1269	**744**	22p multicoloured	..	60	60	☐	☐
1270	**745**	31p multicoloured	..	95	95	☐	☐
1271	**746**	34p multicoloured	..	1·00	1·00	☐	☐
		Set of 5	.. ..	3·00	3·00	☐	☐
		First Day Cover	.. ..		3·00		☐
		Presentation Pack ..	..	3·75		☐	
		PHQ Cards (set of 5)	.. ..	3·00	6·00	☐	☐
		Set of 5 Gutter Pairs	..	6·00		☐	

Collectors Pack 1984

1984 (20 Nov) *Comprises Nos.* 1236/71

	Collectors Pack	.. ..	40·00	☐

Post Office Yearbook

1984 *Comprises Nos.* 1236/71 *in hardbound book with slip case.*

	Yearbook	.. ..	75·00	☐

747 "The Flying Scotsman"

748 "The Golden Arrow"

749 "The Cheltenham Flyer"

750 "The Royal Scot"

751 "The Cornish Riviera"

754 *Decticus verrucivorus* (bush-cricket)

755 *Lucanus cervus* (stag beetle)

756 *Anax imperator* (dragonfly)

Famous Trains

1985 (22 Jan.) *Phosphorised paper*

1272	**747**	17p multicoloured	..	50	50	□	□
1273	**748**	22p multicoloured	..	70	70	□	□
1274	**749**	29p multicoloured	..	90	90	□	□
1275	**750**	31p multicoloured	..	1·00	1·00	□	□
1276	**751**	34p multicoloured	..	1·10	1·10	□	□
		Set of 5		4·00	4·00	□	□
		First Day Cover			5·00		□
		Presentation Pack		4·50		□	
		PHQ Cards (set of 5)		4·00	11·00	□	□
		Set of 5 Gutter Pairs		8·00		□	

Nos. 1272/6 were issued on the occasion of the 150th anniversary of the Great Western Railway Company.

Insects

1985 (12 March) *Phosphorised paper*

1277	**752**	17p multicoloured	..	40	40	□	□
1278	**753**	22p multicoloured	..	60	60	□	□
1279	**754**	29p multicoloured	..	80	80	□	□
1280	**755**	31p multicoloured	..	90	90	□	□
1281	**756**	34p multicoloured	..	90	90	□	□
		Set of 5		3·25	3·25	□	□
		First Day Cover			3·50		□
		Presentation Pack		4·00		□	
		PHQ Cards (set of 5)		3·00	6·50	□	□
		Set of 5 Gutter Pairs		6·50		□	

Nos. 1277/81 were issued on the occasion of the centenaries of the Royal Entomological Society of London's Royal Charter and of the Selborne Society.

752 *Bombus terrestris* (bee)

753 *Coccinella septempunctata* (ladybird)

757 "Water Music", by Handel

758 "The Planets", by Holst

THIRTY·ONE·PENCE

THE·FIRST·CUCKOO
Frederick Delius

THIRTY·FOUR·PENCE

SEA·PICTURES
Edward Elgar

759 "The First Cuckoo", by Delius

760 "Sea Pictures", by Elgar

Europa – European Music Year

1985 (14 MAY) *Phosphorised paper. Perf* 14½

1282	**757**	17p multicoloured	..	65	65	☐	☐
1283	**758**	22p multicoloured		90	90	☐	☐
1284	**759**	31p multicoloured		1·40	1·40	☐	☐
1285	**760**	34p multicoloured		1·50	1·50	☐	☐
		Set of 4	..	..	4·00	4·00	☐ ☐
		First Day Cover				4·00	☐
		Presentation Pack	..	..	4·50		☐
		PHQ Cards (set of 4)	..	..	3·00	6·00	☐ ☐
		Set of 4 Gutter Pairs			8·00		☐

Nos. 1282/5 were issued on the occasion of the 300th birth anniversary of Handel.

761 R.N.L.I. Lifeboat and Signal Flags

762 Beachy Head Lighthouse and Chart

763 "Marecs A" Communications Satellite and Dish Aerials

764 Buoys

Safety at Sea

1985 (18 JUNE) *Phosphorised paper. Perf* 14

1286	**761**	17p multicoloured	..	50	50	☐	☐
1287	**762**	22p multicoloured		65	65	☐	☐
1288	**763**	31p multicoloured		1·10	1·10	☐	☐
1289	**764**	34p multicoloured		1·10	1·10	☐	☐
		Set of 4	..	..	3·00	3·00	☐ ☐
		First Day Cover				3·75	☐
		Presentation Pack	..	..	4·25		☐
		PHQ Cards (set of 4)	..	..	3·00	6·00	☐ ☐
		Set of 4 Gutter Pairs			6·00		☐

Nos. 1286/9 were issued on the occasion of the bicentenary of the unimmersible lifeboat and the 50th anniversary of Radar.

765 Datapost Motorcyclist, City of London

766 Rural Postbus

767 Parcel Delivery in Winter

768 Town Letter Delivery

350 Years of Royal Mail Public Postal Service

1985 (30 JULY) *Phosphorised paper*

1290	**765**	17p multicoloured	..	50	50	☐	☐
1291	**766**	22p multicoloured	..	65	65	☐	☐
1292	**767**	31p multicoloured		1·10	1·10	☐	☐
1293	**768**	34p multicoloured		1·10	1·10	☐	☐
		Set of 4	..	..	3·00	3·00	☐ ☐
		First Day Cover	..	..		4·00	☐
		Presentation Pack	..		4·25		☐
		PHQ Cards (set of 4)	..	..	3·00	6·00	☐ ☐
		Set of 4 Gutter Pairs	..		6·00		☐

769 King Arthur and Merlin

770 The Lady of the Lake

771 Queen Guinevere and Sir Lancelot

772 Sir Galahad

777 Alfred Hitchcock (from photo by Howard Coster)

Arthurian Legends

1985 (3 SEPT.) *Phosphorised paper*

1294	**769**	17p multicoloured	..	50	50	☐	☐
1295	**770**	22p multicoloured	..	65	75	☐	☐
1296	**771**	31p multicoloured	..	1·10	1·10	☐	☐
1297	**772**	34p multicoloured	..	1·10	1·25	☐	☐
		Set of 4	..	3·00	3·25	☐	☐
		First Day Cover			4·00		☐
		Presentation Pack ..	..	4·75		☐	
		PHQ Cards (set of 4)	..	3·00	6·00	☐	☐
		Set of 4 Gutter Pairs ..	..	6·00		☐	

Nos. 1294/7 were issued on the occasion of the 500th anniversary of the printing of Sir Thomas Malory's *Morte d'Arthur*.

British Film Year

1985 (8 OCT.) *Phosphorised paper. Perf 14½*

1298	**773**	17p multicoloured	..	50	50	☐	☐
1299	**774**	22p multicoloured	..	75	75	☐	☐
1300	**775**	29p multicoloured	..	1·10	1·10	☐	☐
1301	**776**	31p multicoloured	..	1·25	1·25	☐	☐
1302	**777**	34p multicoloured	..	1·40	1·40	☐	☐
		Set of 5	..	4·50	4·50	☐	☐
		First Day Cover			4·75		☐
		Presentation Pack	..	6·00		☐	
		Souvenir Book	..	7·00		☐	
		PHQ Cards (set of 5) ..	..	3·00	6·00	☐	☐
		Set of 5 Gutter Pairs ..	..	9·00		☐	

778 Principal Boy

779 Genie

773 Peter Sellers (from photo by Bill Brandt)

774 David Niven (from photo by Cornell Lucas)

780 Dame

781 Good Fairy

775 Charlie Chaplin (from photo by Lord Snowdon)

776 Vivien Leigh (from photo by Angus McBean)

782 Pantomime Cat

Christmas. Pantomime Characters

1985 (19 Nov.) One phosphor band (12p) or phosphorised paper (others)

1303	**778**	12p multicoloured	..	35	30	☐	☐
1304	**779**	17p multicoloured	..	45	40	☐	☐
1305	**780**	22p multicoloured	..	70	80	☐	☐
1306	**781**	31p multicoloured	..	95	1·00	☐	☐
1307	**782**	34p multicoloured	..	1·00	1·10	☐	☐
		Set of 5	.. ..	3·00	3·25	☐	☐
		First Day Cover	.. ..		3·75		☐
		Presentation Pack	.. ..	4·50		☐	
		PHQ Cards (Set of 5)	.. ..	3·00	6·00	☐	☐
		Set of 5 Gutter Pairs	.. ..	6·00		☐	

Collectors Pack 1985

1985 (19 Nov.) Comprises Nos. 1272/1307

	Collectors Pack	.. ..	40·00		☐

Post Office Yearbook

1985 Comprises Nos. 1272/1307 in hardbound book with slip case.

	Yearbook	.. .. ..	75·00		☐

17 PENCE · INDUSTRY YEAR 1986

22 PENCE · INDUSTRY YEAR 1986

783 Light Bulb and North Sea Oil Drilling Rig (Energy)

784 Thermometer and Pharmaceutical Laboratory (Health)

31 PENCE · INDUSTRY YEAR 1986

34 PENCE · INDUSTRY YEAR 1986

785 Garden Hoe and Steel Works (Steel)

786 Loaf of Bread and Cornfield (Agriculture)

Industry Year

1986 (14 Jan.) Phosphorised paper. Perf 14½ × 14

1308	**783**	17p multicoloured	..	45	45	☐	☐
1309	**784**	22p multicoloured	..	60	60	☐	☐
1310	**785**	31p multicoloured	..	90	90	☐	☐
1311	**786**	34p multicoloured	..	1·10	1·10	☐	☐
		Set of 4	.. ..	2·75	2·75	☐	☐
		First Day Cover	.. ..		4·50		☐
		Presentation Pack	..	4·00		☐	
		PHQ Cards (set of 4)	..	3·00	6·00	☐	☐
		Set of 4 Gutter Pairs	..	5·50		☐	

787 Dr. Edmond Halley as Comet

788 *Giotto* Spacecraft approaching Comet

789 "Twice in a Lifetime"

790 Comet orbiting Sun and Planets

Appearance of Halley's Comet

1986 (18 Feb.) Phosphorised paper.

1312	**787**	17p multicoloured	..	45	45	☐	☐
1313	**788**	22p multicoloured	..	70	70	☐	☐
1314	**789**	31p multicoloured	..	1·10	1·10	☐	☐
1315	**790**	34p multicoloured	..	1·10	1·10	☐	☐
		Set of 4	.. ..	3·00	3·00	☐	☐
		First Day Cover	..		4·50		☐
		Presentation Pack	..	4·50		☐	
		PHQ Cards (set of 4)	..	4·00	6·00	☐	☐
		Set of 4 Gutter Pairs	..	6·00		☐	

HER MAJESTY THE QUEEN

Sixtieth Birthday 17p

HER MAJESTY THE QUEEN

Sixtieth Birthday 17p

791 Queen Elizabeth II in 1928, 1942 and 1952

792 Queen Elizabeth II in 1958, 1973 and 1982

Nos. 1316/17 and 1318/19 were each printed together, *se-tenant*, in horizontal pairs throughout the sheets.

60th Birthday of Queen Elizabeth II

1986 (21 Apr.) Phosphorised paper.

1316	**791**	17p multicoloured	..	70	70	☐	☐
		a. Horiz pair.					
		Nos. 1316/17	..	1·40	1·40	☐	☐
1317	**792**	17p multicoloured	..	70	70	☐	☐
1318	**791**	34p multicoloured	..	1·25	1·25	☐	☐
		a. Horiz pair.					
		Nos. 1318/19	..	2·50	2·50	☐	☐
1319	**792**	34p multicoloured	..	1·25	1·25	☐	☐
		Set of 4	..	3·50	3·50	☐	☐
		First Day Cover	..		4·50		☐
		Presentation Pack	..	5·00		☐	
		Souvenir Book	..	7·00		☐	
		PHQ Cards (set of 4)	..	3·00	6·00	☐	☐
		Set of 4 Gutter Pairs	..	7·00		☐	

93 Barn Owl   **794** Pine Marten

95 Wild Cat   **796** Natterjack Toad

Europa. Nature Conservation. Endangered Species

986 (20 MAY) *Phosphorised paper. Perf* $14\frac{1}{2} \times 14$

320	**793**	17p multicoloured	..	50	50	☐	☐
321	**794**	22p multicoloured	..	75	75	☐	☐
322	**795**	31p multicoloured	..	1·10	1·10	☐	☐
323	**796**	34p multicoloured	..	1·25	1·25	☐	☐
		Set of 4	.. .. ..	3·25	3·25	☐	☐
		First Day Cover			4·75		☐
		Presentation Pack	.. ..	4·50		☐	
		PHQ Cards (set of 4)	..	3·00	6·00	☐	☐
		Set of 4 Gutter Pairs	..	6·50		☐	

97 Peasants working in Fields   **798** Freemen working at Town Trades

99 Knight and Retainers   **800** Lord at Banquet

900th Anniversary of Domesday Book

1986 (17 JUNE) *Phosphorised paper*

1324	**797**	17p multicoloured	..	50	50	☐	☐
1325	**798**	22p multicoloured	..	75	75	☐	☐
1326	**799**	31p multicoloured	..	1·10	1·10	☐	☐
1327	**800**	34p multicoloured	..	1·25	1·25	☐	☐
		Set of 4	.. ..	3·25	3·25	☐	☐
		First Day Cover	.. ..		4·25		☐
		Presentation Pack	.. ..	4·50		☐	
		PHQ Cards (set of 4)	.. ..	3·00	6·00	☐	☐
		Set of 4 Gutter Pairs	.. ..	6·50		☐	

801 Athletics   **802** Rowing

803 Weightlifting   **804** Rifle-Shooting

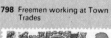

805 Hockey

Thirteenth Commonwealth Games, Edinburgh (Nos. 1328/31) and World Men's Hockey Cup, London (No. 1332)

1986 (15 JULY) *Phosphorised paper.*

1328	**801**	17p multicoloured	..	50	50	☐	☐
1329	**802**	22p multicoloured	..	70	70	☐	☐
1330	**803**	29p multicoloured	..	90	90	☐	☐
1331	**804**	31p multicoloured	..	1·10	1·10	☐	☐
1332	**805**	34p multicoloured	..	1·25	1·25	☐	☐
		Set of 5	.. ..	4·00	4·00	☐	☐
		First Day Cover	.. ..		5·75		☐
		Presentation Pack	.. ..	5·25		☐	
		PHQ Cards (Set of 5)	.. ..	4·00	6·00	☐	☐
		Set of 5 Gutter Pairs	.. ..	8·00		☐	

No. 1332 also marked the centenary of the Hockey Association.

806 Prince Andrew and Miss Sarah Ferguson **807**

Royal Wedding

1986 (22 JULY) *One side band (12p) or phosphorised paper (17p)*

1333	**806**	12p multicoloured	..	60	60	☐	☐
1334	**807**	17p multicoloured	..	90	90	☐	☐
		Set of 2	.. .. ..	1·25	1·25	☐	☐
		First Day Cover	.. ..		2·50		☐
		Presentation Pack	..	2·00		☐	
		PHQ Cards (set of 2)	.. ..	1·50	5·00	☐	☐
		Set of 2 Gutter Pairs	.. ..	2·50		☐	

808 Stylised Cross on Ballot Paper

32nd Commonwealth Parliamentary Conference, London

1986 (19 AUG.) *Phosphorised paper. Perf 14 × 14½*

1335	**808**	34p multicoloured	..	1·25	1·25	☐	☐
		First Day Cover	.. .. ..		2·00		☐
		PHQ Card	.. ..	1·00	2·50	☐	☐
		Gutter Pair	.. .. ..	2·50		☐	

809 Lord Dowding and "Hurricane"   **810** Lord Tedder and "Typhoon"

811 Lord Trenchard and "DH 9A"   **812** Sir Arthur Harris and "Lancaster"

813 Lord Portal and "Mosquito"

History of the Royal Air Force

1986 (16th SEPT.) *Phosphorised paper. Perf 14½ × 14.*

1336	**809**	17p multicoloured	..	50	40	☐	☐
1337	**810**	22p multicoloured	..	70	85	☐	☐
1338	**811**	29p multicoloured	..	90	1·00	☐	☐
1339	**812**	31p multicoloured	..	1·10	1·10	☐	☐
1340	**813**	34p multicoloured	..	1·25	1·25	☐	☐
		Set of 5		4·00	4·25	☐	☐
		First Day Cover	.. ..		5·00		☐
		Presentation Pack	.. ..	6·00		☐	
		PHQ Cards (set of 5)	.. ..	4·00	6·50	☐	☐
		Set of 5 Gutter Pairs	.. ..	8·00		☐	

Nos. 1336/40 were issued to celebrate the 50th anniversary of the first R.A.F. Commands.

814 The Glastonbury Thorn   **815** The Tanad Valley Plygain

816 The Hebrides Tribute   **817** The Dewsbury Church Knell

818 The Hereford Boy Bishop

Christmas. Folk Customs

1986 *One phosphor band (12p, 13p) or phosphorised paper (others)*

1341	**814**	12p mult. (2 Dec.)	..	50	50	☐	☐
1342		13p mult. (18 Nov.)	..	30	30	☐	☐
1343	**815**	18p mult. (18 Nov.)	..	45	45	☐	☐
1344	**816**	22p mult. (18 Nov.)	..	65	65	☐	☐
1345	**817**	31p mult. (18 Nov.)	..	80	80	☐	☐
1346	**818**	34p mult. (18 Nov.)	..	90	90	☐	☐
		Set of 6	..	3·25	3·25	☐	☐
		First Day Covers (2)			5·25		☐
		Presentation Pack (Nos. 1342/6)	5·00			☐	
		PHQ Cards (set of 5) (Nos. 1342/6)		3·00	6·00	☐	☐
		Set of 6 Gutter Pairs		6·50		☐	

Collectors Pack 1986

1986 (18 Nov.) *Comprises Nos.* 1308/40, 1342/6
  Collectors Pack .. .. .. 40·00 ☐

Post Office Yearbook

1986 *Comprises Nos. 1308/40, 1342/6 in hardbound book with slip case.*
  Yearbook .. .. 70·00 ☐

819 North American
Blanket Flower

820 Globe Thistle

821 Echeveria

822 Autumn Crocus

Flower Photographs by Alfred Lammer

1987 (20 Jan.) *Phosphorised paper. Perf* $14\frac{1}{2} \times 14$

1347	**819**	18p multicoloured	..	50	50	☐	☐
1348	**820**	22p multicoloured		70	70	☐	☐
1349	**821**	31p multicoloured		1·10	1·10	☐	☐
1350	**822**	34p multicoloured		1·25	1·25	☐	☐
		Set of 4	..	3·25	3·25	☐	☐
		First Day Cover			4·25		☐
		Presentation Pack ..	..	4·50		☐	
		PHQ Cards (set of 4)	..	3·00	6·00	☐	☐
		Set of 4 Gutter Pairs		6·50		☐	

823 The Principia
Mathematica

824 Motion of Bodies
in Ellipses

825 Optick Treatise

826 The System of
the World

300th Anniversary of The Principia Mathematica by Sir Isaac Newton

1987 (24 Mar.) *Phosphorised paper.*

1351	**823**	18p multicoloured	..	50	50	☐	☐
1352	**824**	22p multicoloured		70	70	☐	☐
1353	**825**	31p multicoloured		1·10	1·10	☐	☐
1354	**826**	34p multicoloured	..	1·25	1·25	☐	☐
		Set of 4	..	3·25	3·25	☐	☐
		First Day Cover ..	..		4·25		☐
		Presentation Pack ..	..	4·50		☐	
		PHQ Cards (set of 4)	..	3·00	6·00	☐	☐
		Set of 4 Gutter Pairs	..	6·50		☐	

For full information on all future British issues, collectors should write to the British Post Office Philatelic Bureau, 20 Brandon Street, Edinburgh EH3 5TT

827 Willis Faber and Dumas Building, Ipswich

828 Pompidou Centre, Paris

829 Staatsgalerie, Stuttgart

830 European Investment Bank, Luxembourg

Europa. British Architects in Europe

1987 (12 MAY) Phosphorised paper.

1355	**827**	18p multicoloured	..	50	50	☐ ☐
1356	**828**	22p multicoloured	..	70	70	☐ ☐
1357	**829**	31p multicoloured	..	1·10	1·10	☐ ☐
1358	**830**	34p multicoloured	..	1·25	1·25	☐ ☐
		Set of 4	.. .. ..	3·25	3·25	☐ ☐
		First Day Cover	.. .. ..		4·25	☐
		Presentation Pack ..	.. ..	4·50		☐
		PHQ Cards (set of 4)	..	3·00	6·00	☐ ☐
		Set of 4 Gutter Pairs	.. ..	6·50		☐

831 Brigade Members with Ashford Litter, 1887

832 Bandaging Blitz Victim, 1940

833 Volunteer with fainting Girl, 1965

834 Transport of Transplant Organ by Air Wing, 1987

Centenary of St. John Ambulance Brigade

1987 (16 JUNE) Phosphorised paper. Perf $14 \times 14\frac{1}{2}$

1359	**831**	18p multicoloured	..	50	50	☐ ☐
1360	**832**	22p multicoloured	..	65	65	☐ ☐
1361	**833**	31p multicoloured	..	1·10	1·10	☐ ☐
1362	**834**	34p multicoloured	..	1·10	1·10	☐ ☐
		Set of 4	.. ..	3·00	3·00	☐ ☐
		First Day Cover	.. ..		4·25	☐
		Presentation Pack ..	..	4·50		☐
		PHQ Cards (set of 4)	.. ..	3·00	6·00	☐ ☐
		Set of 4 Gutter Pairs	.. ..	6·00		☐

835 Arms of the Lord Lyon King of Arms

836 Scottish Heraldic Banner of Prince Charles

837 Arms of Royal Scottish Academy of Painting, Sculpture and Architecture

838 Arms of Royal Society of Edinburgh

300th Anniversary of Revival of Order of the Thistle

1987 (21 JULY) Phosphorised paper. Perf $14\frac{1}{2}$

1363	**835**	18p multicoloured	..	50	50	☐ ☐
1364	**836**	22p multicoloured	..	65	65	☐ ☐
1365	**837**	31p multicoloured	..	1·10	1·10	☐ ☐
1366	**838**	34p multicoloured	..	1·10	1·10	☐ ☐
		Set of 4	.. .. ..	3·00	3·00	☐ ☐
		First Day Cover	.. .. ..		4·25	☐
		Presentation Pack ..	.. ..	4·50		☐
		PHQ Cards (set of 4)	.. ..	3·00	6·00	☐ ☐
		Set of 4 Gutter Pairs	.. ..	6·00		☐

839 Crystal Palace, 'Monarch of the Glen' (Landseer) and Grace Darling

840 Great Eastern, Beeton's Book of Household Management and Prince Albert

841 Albert Memorial, Ballot Box and Disraeli

842 Diamond Jubilee Emblem, Morse Key and Newspaper Placard for Relief of Mafeking

150th Anniversary of Queen Victoria's Accession

1987 (8 Sept.) *Phosphorised paper.*

1367	**839**	18p multicoloured	..	50	50	☐	☐
1368	**840**	22p multicoloured	..	65	65	☐	☐
1369	**841**	31p multicoloured	..	1·10	1·10	☐	☐
1370	**842**	34p multicoloured	..	1·10	1·10	☐	☐
	Set of 4	..	.. ..	3·00	3·00	☐	☐
	First Day Cover	..	..		4·25		☐
	Presentation Pack..	..	..	4·50		☐	
	PHQ Cards (set of 4)	..	..	3·00	6·00	☐	☐
	Set of 4 Gutter Pairs	..	..	6·00		☐	

843 Pot by Bernard Leach

844 Pot by Elizabeth Fritsch

845 Pot by Lucie Rie

846 Pot by Hans Coper

Studio Pottery

1987 (13 Oct.) *Phosphorised paper. Perf* $14\frac{1}{2} \times 14$

1371	**843**	18p multicoloured	..	50	50	☐	☐
1372	**844**	26p multicoloured	..	70	70	☐	☐
1373	**845**	31p multicoloured	..	1·10	1·10	☐	☐
1374	**846**	34p multicoloured	..	1·25	1·25	☐	☐
	Set of 4	..	.. .. ..	3·25	3·25	☐	☐
	First Day Cover	..	..		4·25		☐
	Presentation Pack	..	..	4·50		☐	
	PHQ Cards (set of 4)	..	..	3·00	6·00	☐	☐
	Set of 4 Gutter Pairs	..	..	6·50		☐	

Nos. 1371/4 also mark the birth centenary of Bernard Leach, the potter.

847 Decorating the Christmas tree

848 Waiting for Father Christmas

849 Sleeping Child and Father Christmas in Sleigh

850 Child reading

851 Child playing Flute and Snowman

Christmas

1987 (17 Nov.) *One phosphor band* (13p) *or phosphorised paper* (*others*)

1375	**847**	13p multicoloured	..	30	30	☐	☐
1376	**848**	18p multicoloured	..	50	50	☐	☐
1377	**849**	26p multicoloured	..	75	75	☐	☐
1378	**850**	31p multicoloured	..	95	1·10	☐	☐
1379	**851**	34p multicoloured	..	1·10	1·25	☐	☐
	Set of 5	..	.. ..	3·25	3·50	☐	☐
	First Day Cover	..	..		4·25		☐
	Presentation Pack..	..	..	4·50		☐	
	PHQ Cards (set of 5)	..	..	3·00	6·00	☐	☐
	Set of 5 Gutter Pairs	..	..	6·50		☐	

Collectors Pack 1987

1987 (17 Nov.) *Comprises Nos.* 1347/79
    Collectors Pack .. .. 32·00 ☐

Post Office Yearbook

1987 *Comprises Nos.* 1347/79 *in hardbound book with slip case*
    Yearbook .. .. 45·00 ☐

852 Bull-rout (Jonathan Couch)

853 Yellow Waterlily (Major Joshua Swatkin)

854 Whistling ("Bewick's") Swan (Edward Lear)

855 *Morchella esculenta* (James Sowerby)

Bicentenary of Linnean Society. Archive Illustrations

1988 (19 JAN.) *Phosphorised paper*

1380	**852**	18p multicoloured	..	45	45	☐	☐
1381	**853**	26p multicoloured	..	70	70	☐	☐
1382	**854**	31p multicoloured	..	1·10	1·10	☐	☐
1383	**855**	34p multicoloured	..	1·10	1·10	☐	☐
		Set of 4	..	3·00	3·00	☐	☐
		First Day Cover			4·00		☐
		Presentation Pack ..	..	4·50		☐	
		PHQ Cards (set of 4)	..	3·00	6·00	☐	☐
		Set of 4 Gutter Pairs	..	6·00		☐	

856 Revd William Morgan (Bible translator, 1588)

857 William Salesbury (New Testament translator, 1567)

858 Bishop Richard Davies (New Testament translator, 1567)

859 Bishop Richard Parry (editor of Revised Welsh Bible, 1620)

400th Anniversary of Welsh Bible

1988 (1 MAR.) *Phosphorised paper. Perf* $14\frac{1}{2} \times 14$

1384	**856**	18p multicoloured	..	45	45	☐	☐
1385	**857**	26p multicoloured	..	70	70	☐	☐
1386	**858**	31p multicoloured	..	1·10	1·10	☐	☐
1387	**859**	34p multicoloured	..	1·10	1·10	☐	☐
		Set of 4		3·00	3·00	☐	☐
		First Day Cover			4·00		☐
		Presentation Pack ..	..	4·50		☐	
		PHQ Cards (set of 4)	..	3·00	6·00	☐	☐
		Set of 4 Gutter Pairs	..	6·00		☐	

860 Gymnastics (Centenary of British Amateur Gymnastics Association)

861 Downhill Skiing (Ski Club of Great Britain)

862 Tennis (Centenary of Lawn Tennis Association)

863 Football (Centenary of Football League)

Sports Organizations

1988 (22 MAR.) *Phosphorised paper. Perf 14½*

1388	**860**	18p multicoloured	..	45	45	☐	☐
1389	**861**	26p multicoloured	..	70	70	☐	☐
1390	**862**	31p multicoloured		1·10	1·10	☐	☐
1391	**863**	34p multicoloured		1·10	1·10	☐	☐
		Set of 4	..	3·00	3·00	☐	☐
		First Day Cover	..		4·00		☐
		Presentation Pack	..	4·50		☐	
		PHQ Cards (set of 4) ..	..	2·25	5·00	☐	☐
		Set of 4 Gutter Pairs ..	..	6·00		☐	

864 *Mallard* and Mailbags on Pick-up Arms

865 Loading Transatlantic Mail on Liner *Queen Elizabeth*

866 Glasgow Tram No. 1173 and Pillar Box

867 Imperial Airways Handley Page "HP 42" and Airmail Van

Europa. Transport and Mail Services in 1930's

1988 (10 MAY) *Phosphorised paper*

1392	**864**	18p multicoloured	..	50	50	☐	☐
1393	**865**	26p multicoloured	..	80	80	☐	☐
1394	**866**	31p multicoloured	..	1·10	1·10	☐	☐
1395	**867**	34p multicoloured	..	1·25	1·25	☐	☐
		Set of 4	..	3·25	3·25	☐	☐
		First Day Cover ..	..		4·25		☐
		Presentation Pack ..	..	4·50		☐	
		PHQ Cards (set of 4) ..	..	2·00	5·00	☐	☐
		Set of 4 Gutter Pairs ..	..	6·50		☐	

868 Early Settler and Sailing Clipper

869 Queen Elizabeth II with British and Australian Parliament Buildings

870 W. G. Grace (cricketer) and Tennis Racquet

871 Shakespeare, John Lennon (entertainer) and Sydney Landmarks

Nos. 1396/7 and 1398/9 were each printed together, *se-tenant*, in horizontal pairs throughout the sheets, each pair showing a background design of the Australian flag.

Bicentenary of Australian Settlement

1988 (21 JUNE) *Phosphorised paper. Perf 14½*

1396	**868**	18p multicoloured	..	60	60	☐	☐
		a. Horiz pair.					
		Nos. 1396/7 ..	..	1·25	1·25	☐	☐
1397	**869**	18p multicoloured	..	60	60	☐	☐
1398	**870**	34p multicoloured	..	1·10	1·10	☐	☐
		a. Horiz pair.					
		Nos. 1398/9 ..	..	2·40	2·40	☐	☐
1399	**871**	34p multicoloured	..	1·10	1·10	☐	☐
		Set of 4	..	3·25	3·25	☐	☐
		First Day Cover ..	..		4·25		☐
		Presentation Pack ..	..	4·50		☐	
		Souvenir Book ..	..	6·00		☐	
		PHQ Cards (set of 4) ..	..	2·00	5·00	☐	☐
		Set of 4 Gutter Pairs ..	..	6·50		☐	

Stamps in similar designs were also issued by Australia.

872 Spanish Galeasse off The Lizard

873 English Fleet leaving Plymouth

874 Engagement off Isle of Wight

875 Attack of English Fire-ships, Calais

876 Armada in Storm,
North Sea

Nos. 1400/4 were printed together, *se-tenant*, in horizontal strips of 5 throughout the sheet, forming a composite design.

400th Anniversary of Spanish Armada

1988 (19 JULY) *Phosphorised paper*

1400	**872**	18p multicoloured	..	65	65	☐	☐
		a. Horiz strip of 5.					
		Nos. 1400/4 ..	..	2·75	2·75	☐	☐
1401	**873**	18p multicoloured	..	65	65	☐	☐
1402	**874**	18p multicoloured	..	65	65	☐	☐
1403	**875**	18p multicoloured	..	65	65	☐	☐
1404	**876**	18p multicoloured	..	65	65	☐	☐
		Set of 5	..	2·75	2·75	☐	☐
		First Day Cover	..		3·75		☐
		Presentation Pack ..	..	4·00		☐	
		PHQ Cards (set of 5)	..	2·50	5·50	☐	☐
		Gutter strip of 10	.. ..	5·50		☐	

877 "The Owl and the
Pussy-cat"

878 "Edward Lear as a Bird"
(self-portrait)

879 "Cat" (from alphabet
book)

880 "There was a Young Lady
whose Bonnet . . ."
(limerick)

Death Centenary of Edward Lear (artist and author)

1988 (6–27 SEPT.) *Phosphorised paper*

1405	**877**	19p black, pale cream and carmine	50	50	☐	☐
1406	**878**	27p black, pale cream and yellow	65	80	☐	☐
1407	**879**	32p black, pale cream and emerald	1·10	1·10	☐	☐
1408	**880**	35p black, pale cream and blue	1·10	1·25	☐	☐
		Set of 4	3·00	3·25	☐	☐
		First Day Cover		4·00		☐
		Presentation Pack	4·50		☐	
		PHQ Cards (set of 4) ..	2·00	5·00	☐	☐
		Set of 4 Gutter Pairs	6·00		☐	
MS1409		122 × 90 mm. Nos. 1405/8	8·00	8·50	☐	☐
		First Day Cover (27 Sept.) ..		8·50		☐

No. **MS**1409 was sold at £1·35, the premium being used for the "Stamp World London 90" International Stamp Exhibition.

881 Carrickfergus Castle

882 Caernarvon Castle

883 Edinburgh Castle

884 Windsor Castle

1988 (18 OCT.) *Ordinary paper*

1410	**881**	£1 deep green	..	2·50	50	☐	☐
1411	**882**	£1·50 maroon	.. ..	3·50	1·00	☐	☐
1412	**883**	£2 indigo	.. ..	5·00	1·50	☐	☐
1413	**884**	£5 deep brown	.. ..	12·00	3·00	☐	☐
		Set of 4	..	21·00	5·50	☐	☐
		First Day Cover	..		45·00		☐
		Presentation Pack ..	..	22·00		☐	
		Set of 4 Gutter Pairs	.. ..	42·00		☐	

For similar designs, but with silhouette Queen's head see Nos. 1611/14.

885 Journey to Bethlehem

886 Shepherds and Star

887 Three Wise Men

888 Nativity

889 The Annunciation

890 Atlantic Puffin

891 Avocet

892 Oystercatcher

893 Northern Gannet

Christmas

1988 (15 Nov.) *One phosphor band* (14p) *or phosphorised paper* (others)

1414	**885**	14p multicoloured	..	35	35	☐ ☐
1415	**886**	19p multicoloured	..	40	45	☐ ☐
1416	**887**	27p multicoloured	..	70	70	☐ ☐
1417	**888**	32p multicoloured	..	90	1·00	☐ ☐
1418	**889**	35p multicoloured	..	1·00	1·10	☐ ☐
		Set of 5	..	3·00	3·25	☐ ☐
		First Day Cover			4·25	☐
		Presentation Pack ..		4·25		☐
		PHQ Cards (set of 5)	..	2·50	5·25	☐ ☐
		Set of 5 Gutter Pairs	..	.. · 6·00		☐

Collectors Pack 1988

1988 (15 Nov.) *Comprises Nos.* 1380/1408, 1414/18

	Collectors Pack	.. .. .. 32·00	☐

Post Office Yearbook

1988 *Comprises Nos.* 1380/1404. **MS**1409, 1414/18 *in hardbound book with slip case*

	Yearbook	.. .. 40·00	☐

Centenary of Royal Society for the Protection of Birds

1989 (17 Jan.) *Phosphorised paper*

1419	**890**	19p multicoloured	..	45	45	☐ ☐
1420	**891**	27p multicoloured	..	1·10	1·10	☐ ☐
1421	**892**	32p multicoloured	..	1·10	1·10	☐ ☐
1422	**893**	35p multicoloured	..	1·25	1·25	☐ ☐
		Set of 4		3·50	3·50	☐ ☐
		First Day Cover			4·50	☐
		Presentation Pack		4·50		☐
		PHQ Cards (set of 4)		2·50	5·00	☐ ☐
		Set of 4 Gutter Pairs		7·00		☐

894 Rose

895 Cupid

896 Yachts

897 Fruit

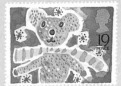

898 Teddy Bear

Nos. 1423/7 were printed together, *se-tenant*, in horizontal strips of five, two such strips forming the booklet pane with twelve half stamp-size labels.

Greetings Booklet Stamps

1989 (31 Jan.) *Phosphorised paper*

1423	**894**	19p multicoloured	..	2·75	2·25	☐ ☐
		a. *Booklet pane.*				
		Nos. 1423/7 × 2	..	24·00		☐
1424	**895**	19p multicoloured	..	2·75	2·25	☐ ☐
1425	**896**	19p multicoloured	..	2·75	2·25	☐ ☐
1426	**897**	19p multicoloured	..	2·75	2·25	☐ ☐
1427	**898**	19p multicoloured	..	2·75	2·25	☐ ☐
		Set of 5	..	12·00	10·00	☐ ☐
		First Day Cover			10·00	☐

899 Fruit and Vegetables

900 Meat Products

901 Dairy Produce

902 Cereal Products

Food and Farming Year

1989 (7 Mar.) *Phosphorised paper. Perf* 14 × 14½

1428	**899**	19p multicoloured	..	50	50	☐ ☐
1429	**900**	27p multicoloured	..	80	80	☐ ☐
1430	**901**	32p multicoloured	..	1·10	1·10	☐ ☐
1431	**902**	35p multicoloured	..	1·25	1·25	☐ ☐
		Set of 4	..	3·25	3·25	☐ ☐
		First Day Cover			4·25	☐
		Presentation Pack	..	4·50		☐
		PHQ Cards (set of 4) ..	..	2·00	5·00	☐ ☐
		Set of 4 Gutter Pairs ..	..	6·50		☐

903 Mortar Board (150th Anniv of Public Education in England)

904 Cross on Ballot Paper (3rd Direct Elections to European Parliament)

905 Posthorn (26th Postal, Telegraph and Telephone International Congress Brighton)

906 Globe (Inter-Parliamentary Union Centenary Conference, London)

Nos. 1432/3 and 1434/5 were each printed together, *se-tenant*, in horizontal pairs throughout the sheets.

Anniversaries

1989 (11 Apr.) *Phosphorised paper. Perf* 14 × 14½

1432	**903**	19p multicoloured	..	1·25	1·25	☐ ☐
		a. *Horiz pair.*				
		Nos. 1432/3	..	2·50	2·50	☐ ☐
1433	**904**	19p multicoloured	..	1·25	1·25	☐ ☐
1434	**905**	35p multicoloured	..	1·75	1·75	☐ ☐
		a. *Horiz pair.*				
		Nos. 1434/5	..	3·50	3·50	☐ ☐
1435	**906**	35p multicoloured	..	1·75	1·75	☐ ☐
		Set of 4		5·50	5·50	☐ ☐
		First Day Cover			6·50	☐
		Presentation Pack		6·00		☐
		PHQ Cards (set of 4)		2·00	7·00	☐ ☐
		Set of 2 Gutter Pairs		5·75		☐

907 Toy Train and Airplane

908 Building Bricks

909 Dice and Board Games

910 Toy Robot, Boat and Doll's House

Europa. Games and Toys

1989 (16 MAY) *Phosphorised paper*

1436	**907**	19p multicoloured	..	50	50	☐	☐
1437	**908**	27p multicoloured	..	90	90	☐	☐
1438	**909**	32p multicoloured	..	1·25	1·25	☐	☐
1439	**910**	35p multicoloured	..	1·40	1·40	☐	☐
	Set of 4	.. ..		3·50	3·50	☐	☐
	First Day Cover	.. ..			4·25		☐
	Presentation Pack	.. ..		4·50		☐	
	PHQ Cards (set of 4)	..	..	2·00	5·00	☐	☐
	Set of 4 Gutter Pairs	..	..	7·00		☐	

911 Ironbridge, Shropshire

912 Tin Mine, St. Agnes Head, Cornwall

913 Cotton Mills, New Lanark, Strathclyde

914 Pontcysyllte Aqueduct, Clwyd

915

Industrial Archaeology

1989 (4–25 JULY) *Phosphorised paper*

1440	**911**	19p multicoloured	..	50	50	☐	☐
1441	**912**	27p multicoloured	..	80	80	☐	☐
1442	**913**	32p multicoloured	..	1·00	1·00	☐	☐
1443	**914**	35p multicoloured	..	1·10	1·10	☐	☐
	Set of 4	.. .. ..	..	3·00	3·00	☐	☐
	First Day Cover	.. ..			4·25		☐
	Presentation Pack	..	..	4·50		☐	
	PHQ Cards (set of 4)	..	..	2·00	5·00	☐	☐
	Set of 4 Gutter Pairs		..	6·50		☐	
MS1444	122 × 90 mm. **915** As Nos.						
	1440/3 but designs horizontal			6·00	6·00	☐	☐
	First Day Cover (25 July)		..		6·00		☐

No.**MS**1444 was sold at £1·40, the premium being used for the "Stamp World London 90" International Stamp Exhibition.

916

917

Booklet Stamps

1989 (22 AUG.)–**92**

(a) Printed in photogravure by Harrison and Sons. Perf 15 × 14

1445	**916**	(2nd) bright blue (1 centre band)	.. ..	60	35	☐	☐
1446		(2nd) bright blue (1 side band) (20.3.90)	.. ..	2·25	2·25	☐	☐
1447	**917**	(1st) black (phosphorised paper)	.. .. ..	1·00	50	☐	☐
1448		(1st) brownish black (2 bands) (20.3.90)	.. ..	2·25	2·25	☐	☐

(b) Printed in lithography by Walsall. Perf 14

1449	**916**	(2nd) bright blue (1 centre band)	.. ..	50	
1450	**917**	(1st) black (2 bands)	..	2·00	

(c) Printed in lithography by Questa. Perf 15 × 14

1451	**916**	(2nd) bright blue (1 centre band) (19.9.89)	50	35	☐	☐
1451*a*		(2nd) bright blue (1 side band) (25.2.92) ..	1·00	1·00	☐	☐
1452	**917**	(1st) black (phosphorised paper) (19.9.89)	1·10	1·10	☐	☐
		First Day Cover (Nos. 1445, 1447)		3·50	☐	

For similar stamps showing changed colours see Nos. 1511/16 and for those with elliptical perforations Nos. 1663*a*/6.

No. 1451*a* exists with the phosphor band at the left or right of the stamp.

922 Royal Mail Coach

923 Escort of Blues and Royals

924 Lord Mayor's Coach

925 Coach Team passing St Paul's

918 Snowflake (× 10)

919 *Calliphora erythrocephala* (fly) (× 5)

920 Blood Cells (× 500)

921 Microchip (× 600)

926 Blues and Royals Drum Horse

Nos. 1457/61 were printed together, *se-tenant*, in horizontal strips of 5 throughout the sheet, forming a composite design.

150th Anniversary of Royal Microscopical Society

1989 (5 SEPT.) *Phosphorised paper. Perf 14½ × 14*

1453	**918**	19p multicoloured	..	50	50	☐	☐
1454	**919**	27p multicoloured	..	85	85	☐	☐
1455	**920**	32p multicoloured	..	1·25	1·25	☐	☐
1456	**921**	35p multicoloured	..	1·40	1·40	☐	☐
		Set of 4		3·50	3·50	☐	☐
		First Day Cover			5·00		☐
		Presentation Pack		4·00		☐	
		PHQ Cards (set of 4) ..		2·00	5·00	☐	☐
		Set of 4 Gutter Pairs		7·00		☐	

Lord Mayor's Show, London

1989 (17 OCT.) *Phosphorised paper*

1457	**922**	20p multicoloured	..	60	60	☐	☐
		a. Horiz strip of 5. Nos. 1457/61		3·25	3·25	☐	☐
1458	**923**	20p multicoloured	..	60	60	☐	☐
1459	**924**	20p multicoloured	..	60	60	☐	☐
1460	**925**	20p multicoloured	..	60	60	☐	☐
1461	**926**	20p multicoloured	..	60	60	☐	☐
		Set of 5		3·25	2·75	☐	☐
		First Day Cover			3·75		☐
		Presentation Pack		4·50		☐	
		PHQ Cards (set of 5) ..		2·50	5·00	☐	☐
		Gutter Strip of 10		6·50		☐	

Nos. 1457/61 commemorate the 800th anniversary of the installation of the first Lord Mayor of London.

927 14th-century Peasants from Stained-glass Window

928 Arches and Roundels, West Front

929 Octagon Tower

930 Arcade from West Transept

931 Triple Arch from West Front

Christmas. 800th Anniversary of Ely Cathedral

1989 (14 Nov.) *One phosphor band (Nos. 1462/3) or phosphorised paper (others)*

1462	927	15p gold, silver and blue	35	35 □ □
1463	928	15p + 1p gold, silver and blue	50	40 □ □
1464	929	20p + 1p gold, silver and rosine	60	50 □ □
1465	930	34p + 1p gold, silver and emerald	1·25	1·40 □ □
1466	931	37p + 1p gold, silver and yellow-olive	1·25	1·40 □ □
		Set of 5	3·50	3·50 □ □
		First Day Cover		4·00 □
		Presentation Pack	4·50	□
		PHQ Cards (set of 5)	2·50	5·00 □ □
		Set of 5 Gutter Pairs	7·00	□

Collectors Pack 1989

1989 (14 Nov.) *Comprises Nos. 1419/22, 1428/43 and 1453/66*

	Collectors Pack	32·00	□

Post Office Yearbook

1989 (14 Nov.) *Comprises Nos. 1419/22, 1428/44 and 1453/66 in hardback book with slip case.*

	Yearbook	45·00	□

932 Queen Victoria and Queen Elizabeth II

150th Anniversary of the Penny Black

1990 (10 Jan.–12 June)

(a) Printed in photogravure by Harrison and Sons. Perf 15 × 14

1467	932	15p bright blue (1 centre band)	50	50 □ □
1468		15p bright blue (1 side band) (30 Jan)	1·50	1·50 □ □
1469		20p brownish black and cream (phosphorised paper)	75	75 □ □
1470		20p brnish blk & cream (2 bands) (30 Jan)	1·50	1·50 □ □
1471		29p deep mauve (phosphorised paper)	1·00	1·00 □ □
1472		29p deep mauve (2 bands) (20 Mar)	5·00	5·00 □ □
1473		34p deep bluish grey (phosphorised paper)	1·25	1·25 □ □
1474		37p rosine (phosphorised paper)	1·40	1·40 □ □
		Set of 5 (Nos. 1467, 1469, 1471, 1473/4)	4·50	4·50 □ □
		First Day Cover (Nos. 1467, 1469, 1471, 1473/4)		6·00 □
		Presentation Pack (Nos. 1467, 1469, 1471, 1473/4)	5·75	□

(b) Litho Walsall. Perf 14 (30 Jan)

1475	932	15p bright blue (1 centre band)	80	60 □ □
1476		20p brnish blk & cream (phosphorised paper)	90	80 □ □

(c) Litho Questa. Perf 15 × 14 (17 Apr)

1477	932	15p bright blue (1 centre band)	1·25	1·25 □ □
1478		20p brnish black (phosphorised paper)	1·25	1·25 □ □

No. 1468 exists with the phosphor band at the left or right of the stamp.

933 Kitten

934 Rabbit

935 Duckling

936 Puppy

150th Anniversary of Royal Society for Prevention of Cruelty to Animals

1990 (23 Jan.) *Phosphorised paper. Perf* 14 × 14½.

1479	**933**	20p multicoloured	..	65	50	☐	☐
1480	**934**	29p multicoloured	..	1·00	80	☐	☐
1481	**935**	34p multicoloured	..	1·40	1·10	☐	☐
1482	**936**	37p multicoloured	..	1·40	1·10	☐	☐
		Set of 4		4·00	3·25	☐	☐
		First Day Cover			5·25	☐	
		Presentation Pack		5·00		☐	
		PHQ Cards (set of 4)		2·50	5·50	☐	☐
		Set of 4 Gutter Pairs		8·00		☐	

937 Teddy Bear

938 Dennis the Menace

939 Punch

940 Cheshire Cat

941 The Man in the Moon

942 The Laughing Policeman

943 Clown

944 Mona Lisa

945 Queen of Hearts

946 Stan Laurel (comedian)

T **937**/46 were printed together, *se-tenant*, in booklet panes of 10.

Greetings Booklet Stamps. "Smiles"

1990 (6 Feb.) *Two phosphor bands*

1483	**937**	20p multicoloured	..	2·25	1·25	☐	☐
		a. Booklet pane.					
		Nos. 1483/92	..	20·00		☐	
1484	**938**	20p multicoloured	..	2·25	1·25	☐	☐
1485	**939**	20p multicoloured	..	2·25	1·25	☐	☐
1486	**940**	20p multicoloured	..	2·25	1·25	☐	☐
1487	**941**	20p multicoloured	..	2·25	1·25	☐	☐
1488	**942**	20p multicoloured	..	2·25	1·25	☐	☐
1489	**943**	20p multicoloured	..	2·25	1·25	☐	☐
1490	**944**	20p multicoloured	..	2·25	1·25	☐	☐
1491	**945**	20p multicoloured	..	2·25	1·25	☐	☐
1492	**946**	20p gold and grey-black	..	2·25	1·25	☐	☐
		Set of 10		20·00	11·00	☐	☐
		First Day Cover			12·00		☐

For those designs with the face value expressed as "1st" see Nos. 1550/9.

947 Alexandra Palace ("Stamp World London 90" Exhibition)

948 Glasgow School of Art

949 British Philatelic Bureau,
Edinburgh

950 Templeton Carpet Factory,
Glasgow

953

"Stamp World 90" International Stamp Exhibition, London

Europa (Nos. 1493 and 1495) and "Glasgow 1990 European City of Culture" (Nos. 1494 and 1496)

1990 (6 MAR.) *Phosphorised paper*

1493	**947**	20p multicoloured	..	50	50	☐	☐
1494	**948**	20p multicoloured		50	50	☐	☐
1495	**949**	29p multicoloured	..	1·10	1·10	☐	☐
1496	**950**	37p multicoloured	..	1·25	1·25	☐	☐
		Set of 4		3·00	3·00	☐	☐
		First Day Cover			4·25		☐
		Presentation Pack ..		4·00		☐	
		PHQ Cards (set of 4)		2·50	5·25	☐	☐
		Set of 4 Gutter Pairs		6·00		☐	

1990 (3 MAY.) *Sheet* 122 × 90 *mm. Phosphorised paper*

MS1501	**953**	20p. brownish black and cream	.. ..	4·00	4·00	☐	☐
		First Day Cover			5·50		☐
		Souvenir Book (Nos. 1467, 1469, 1471, 1473/4 and **MS**1501)		..12·00			☐

No. **MS**1501 was sold at £1, the premium being used for the exhibition.

951 Export Achievement
Award

952 Technological
Achievement Award

Nos. 1497/8 and 1499/500 were each printed together, *se-tenant*, in horizontal pairs throughout the sheets.

25th Anniversary of Queen's Awards for Export and Technology

1990 (10 APR.) *Phosphorised paper. Perf* 14 × 14½.

1497	**951**	20p multicoloured	..	70	70	☐	☐
		a. *Horiz pair.* Nos. 1497/8 ..	..	1·40	1·40	☐	☐
1498	**952**	20p multicoloured		70	70	☐	☐
1499	**951**	37p multicoloured		1·25	1·25	☐	☐
		a. *Horiz pair.* Nos. 1499/500 ..	..	2·50	2·50	☐	☐
1500	**952**	37p multicoloured		1·25	1·25	☐	☐
		Set of 4		3·50	3·50	☐	☐
		First Day Cover			4·50		☐
		Presentation Pack ..	..	4·00		☐	
		PHQ Cards (set of 4)	..	2·50	5·25	☐	☐
		Set of 2 Gutter Pairs		3·75		☐	

954 Cycad and Sir Joseph
Banks Building

955 Stone Pine and Princess
of Wales Conservatory

956 Willow Tree and Palm
House

957 Cedar Tree and Pagoda

150th Anniversary of Kew Gardens

1990 (5 JUNE) *Phosphorised paper*

1502	**954**	20p multicoloured	..	50	50	☐	☐
1503	**955**	29p multicoloured	..	80	80	☐	☐

1504	**956**	34p multicoloured	..	1·10	1·25	☐	☐
1505	**957**	37p multicoloured	..	1·25	1·40	☐	☐
		Set of 4	.. .. ..	3·25	3·50	☐	☐
		First Day Cover	.. ..		4·50		☐
		Presentation Pack	.. ..	4·00		☐	
		PHQ Cards (set of 4)	.. ..	2·50	5·00	☐	☐
		Set of 4 Gutter Pairs	..	6·50		☐	

958 Thomas Hardy and Clyffe Clump, Dorset

150th Birth Anniversary of Thomas Hardy (author)

1990 (10 July) Phosphorised paper

1506	**958**	20p multicoloured	..	60	70	☐	☐
		First Day Cover	.. ..		2·00		☐
		Presentation Pack	.. ..	1·75		☐	
		PHQ Card	.. ..	75	2·00	☐	☐
		Gutter Pair	.. ..	1·25		☐	

959 Queen Elizabeth the Queen Mother

960 Queen Elizabeth

961 Elizabeth, Duchess of York

962 Lady Elizabeth Bowes-Lyon

90th Birthday of Queen Elizabeth the Queen Mother

1990 (2 Aug.) Phosphorised paper

1507	**959**	20p multicoloured		50	50	☐	☐
1508	**960**	29p silver, indigo and					
		grey-blue	..	80	80	☐	☐

1509	**961**	34p multicoloured	..	1·10	1·25	☐	☐
1510	**962**	37p silver, sepia and					
		stone	..	1·25	1·40	☐	☐
		Set of 4	.. ..	3·25	3·50	☐	☐
		First Day Cover	.. ..		4·75		☐
		Presentation Pack	.. ..	4·50		☐	
		PHQ Cards (set of 4)	..	2·50	5·50	☐	☐
		Set of 4 Gutter Pairs ..	..	6·50		☐	

Booklet Stamps

1990 (7 Aug.)-**92** As Types **916/17**, but colours changed

(a) Photo Harrison, Perf 15 × 14

1511	**916**	(2nd) dp blue (1 centre					
		band)	60	50	☐	☐
1512	**917**	(1st) brt orge-red (phos-					
		phorised paper) ..	60	50	☐	☐

(b) Litho Questa. Perf 15 × 14

1513	**916**	(2nd) dp blue (1 centre					
		band) ..	1·25	1·25	☐	☐
1514	**917**	(1st) brt orge-red (phos-					
		phorised paper) ..	60	60	☐	☐
1514a		(1st) brt orange-red (2					
		bands) (25.2.92)	1·00	1·00	☐	☐

(c) Litho Walsall. Perf 14

1515	**916**	(2nd) dp blue (1 centre					
		band)	60	60	☐	
1516	**917**	(1st) brt orge-red (phos-					
		phorised paper)	60	60		
		c. Perf 13	3·00	2·00	☐	☐
		First Day Cover (Nos. 1515/					
		16)		3·00		☐

For similar stamps with elliptical perforations see Nos. 1663a/6.

963 Victoria Cross

964 George Cross

965 Distinguished Service Cross and Distinguished Service Medal

966 Military Cross and Military Medal

992 Michael Faraday
(inventor of
electric motor)
(Birth Bicentenary)

993 Charles Babbage
(computer
science pioneer)
(Birth Bicentenary)

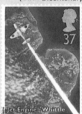

994 Radar Sweep of
East Anglia (50th
Anniv of Discovery
by Sir Robert
Watson-Watt)

995 Gloster E28/39
Aircraft over East
Anglia (50th
Anniv of First
Flight of Sir Frank
Whittle's Jet Engine)

Scientific Achievements

1991 (5 MAR.) *Phosphorised paper*

1546	**992**	22p multicoloured	..	65	65	□ □
1547	**993**	22p multicoloured	..	65	65	□ □
1548	**994**	31p multicoloured	..	95	95	□ □
1549	**995**	37p multicoloured	..	1·10	1·10	□ □
	Set of 4	.. .. ..	..	3·00	3·00	□ □
	First Day Cover	.. ..	..		4·00	□
	Presentation Pack	..	..	3·75		□
	PHQ Cards (set of 4)	..	..	3·00	5·50	□ □
	Set of 4 Gutter Pairs	..	..	6·00		□

996 Teddy Bear

Nos. 1550/9 were printed together, *se-tenant,* in booklet panes of 10
stamps and 12 half stamp-size labels.

Greetings Booklet Stamps. "Smiles"

1991 (26 MAR.) *As Nos. 1483/92, but inscribed "1st" as
T 996. Two phosphor bands.*

1550	**996**	(1st) multicoloured	..	40	45	□ □
		a. Booklet pane. Nos.				
		1550/9	.. .. ..	3·50		□
1551	**938**	(1st) multicoloured	..	40	45	□ □
1552	**939**	(1st) multicoloured	..	40	45	□ □
1553	**940**	(1st) multicoloured	..	40	45	□ □
1554	**941**	(1st) multicoloured	..	40	45	□ □
1555	**942**	(1st) multicoloured	..	40	45	□ □
1556	**943**	(1st) multicoloured	..	40	45	□ □
1557	**944**	(1st) multicoloured	..	40	45	□ □
1558	**945**	(1st) multicoloured	..	40	45	□ □
1559	**946**	(1st) multicoloured	..	40	45	□ □
	Set of 10	.. ..	..	3·50	4·00	□ □
	First Day Cover ..	.. ..	..		7·50	□

997 Man looking at Space **998**

999 Space looking at Man **1000**

Nos. 1560/1 and 1562/3 were each printed together, *se-tenant,* in horizontal pairs throughout the sheets, each pair forming a composite design.

Europa. Europe in Space

1991 (23 APR.) *Phosphorised paper.*

1560	**997**	22p multicoloured	..	55	55	□ □
		a. Horiz pair. Nos. 1560/1		1·10	1·10	□ □
1561	**998**	22p multicoloured	..	55	55	□ □
1562	**999**	37p multicoloured	..	1·10	1·10	□ □
		a. Horiz pair. Nos. 1562/3		2·25	2·25	□ □
1563	**1000**	37p multicoloured	..	1·10	1·10	□ □
	Set of 4	.. .. ..	..	3·00	3·00	□ □
	First Day Cover	.. ..	..		4·00	□
	Presentation Pack		..	4·00		□
	PHQ Cards (set of 4)	..	..	3·00	5·50	□ □
	Set of 2 Gutter Pairs	..	..	6·00		□

1001 Fencing

1002 Hurdling

1003 Diving

1004 Rugby

World Student Games, Sheffield (Nos. 1564/6) and World Cup Rugby Championship, London (No. 1567)

1991 (11 JUNE) *Phosphorised paper. Perf* 14½ × 14

1564	**1001**	22p multicoloured	..	50	50	☐	☐
1565	**1002**	26p multicoloured	..	80	80	☐	☐
1566	**1003**	31p multicoloured	..	95	95	☐	☐
1567	**1004**	37p multicoloured	..	1·10	1·10	☐	☐
	Set of 4	.. .. ..	..	3·00	3·00	☐	☐
	First Day Cover	.. ..			4·00		☐
	Presentation Pack	.. ..		4·00			☐
	PHQ Cards (set of 4)	.. ..		3·00	5·50		☐
	Set of 4 Gutter Pairs	.. ..		6·00			☐

1005 "Silver Jubilee"

1006 "Mme Alfred Carrière"

1007 *Rosa moyesii*

1008 "Harvest Fayre"

1009 "Mutabilis"

9th World Congress of Roses, Belfast

1991 (16 JULY) *Phosphorised paper. Perf* 14½ × 14

1568	**1005**	22p multicoloured		75	50	☐	☐
1569	**1006**	26p multicoloured		80	80	☐	☐
1570	**1007**	31p multicoloured		85	85	☐	☐
1571	**1008**	33p multicoloured		95	95	☐	☐
1572	**1009**	37p multicoloured		1·10	1·25	☐	☐
	Set of 5	.. ..	..	4·00	4·00	☐	☐
	First Day Cover	..	..		5·50		☐
	Presentation Pack		..	4·50			☐
	PHQ Cards (set of 5)		..	3·25	6·50	☐	☐
	Set of 5 Gutter Pairs		..	8·00			☐

1010 Iguanodon

1011 Stegosaurus

1012 Tyrannosaurus

1013 Protoceratops

1014 Triceratops

150th Anniversary of Dinosaurs' Identification by Owen

1991 (20 Aug.) *Phosphorised paper. Perf* $14\frac{1}{2} \times 14$

1573	1010	22p multicoloured	..	75	50	☐	☐
1574	1011	26p multicoloured	..	90	1·00	☐	☐
1575	1012	31p multicoloured	..	1·00	1·10	☐	☐
1576	1013	33p multicoloured	..	1·10	1·10	☐	☐
1577	1014	37p multicoloured	..	1·25	1·25	☐	☐
		Set of 5	..	4·50	4·50	☐	☐
		First Day Cover	..		5·50		☐
		Presentation Pack ..	..	5·50		☐	
		PHQ Cards (set of 5) ..	..	3·25	6·00	☐	☐
		Set of 5 Gutter Pairs ..	..	9·00		☐	

1015 Map of 1816

1016 Map of 1906

1017 Map of 1959

1018 Map of 1991

Bicentenary of Ordnance Survey. Maps of Hamstreet, Kent

1991 (17 Sept.) *Phosphorised paper. Perf* $14\frac{1}{2} \times 14$

1578	1015	24p multicoloured	..	50	50	☐	☐
1579	1016	28p multicoloured	..	80	85	☐	☐
1580	1017	33p multicoloured	..	95	1·00	☐	☐
1581	1018	39p multicoloured	..	1·10	1·25	☐	☐
		Set of 4	..	3·00	3·25	☐	☐
		First Day Cover	..		4·25		☐
		Presentation Pack ..	..	4·00		☐	
		PHQ Cards (set of 4) ..	..	3·00	6·00	☐	☐
		Set of 4 Gutter Pairs ..	..	6·00		☐	

1019 Adoration of the Magi

1020 Mary and Baby Jesus in the Stable

1021 The Holy Family and Angel

1022 The Annunciation

1023 The Flight into Egypt

Christmas. Illuminated Manuscripts from the Bodleian Library, Oxford

1991 (12 Nov.) *One phosphor band (18p) or phosphorised paper (others)*

1582	1019	18p multicoloured	..	70	40	☐	☐
1583	1020	24p multicoloured	..	80	50	☐	☐
1584	1021	28p multicoloured	..	85	1·00	☐	☐
1585	1022	33p multicoloured	..	95	1·10	☐	☐
1586	1023	39p multicoloured	..	1·10	1·40	☐	☐
		Set of 5		4·00	4·00	☐	☐
		First Day Cover			4·50		☐
		Presentation Pack ..		4·25		☐	
		PHQ Cards (set of 5) ..	..	3·00	6·00	☐	☐
		Set of 5 Gutter Pairs ..	..	8·00		☐	

Collectors Pack 1991

1991 (12 Nov.) *Comprises Nos.* 1531/5, 1546/9 *and* 1560/86.

Collectors Pack	28·00	☐

Post Office Yearbook

1991 *Comprises Nos.* 1531/5, 1546/9 *and* 1560/86. *in hardback book with slip case.*

Yearbook	50·00	☐

1024 Fallow Deer in Scottish Forest

1025 Hare on North Yorkshire Moors

1026 Fox in the Fens

1027 Redwing and Home Counties Village

1028 Welsh Mountain Sheep in Snowdonia

The Four Seasons. Wintertime

1992 (14 Jan.) One phosphor band (18p) or phosphorised paper (others)

1587	**1024**	18p multicoloured	..	45	50	□ □
1588	**1025**	24p multicoloured	..	60	65	□ □
1589	**1026**	28p multicoloured	..	70	75	□ □
1590	**1027**	33p multicoloured	..	85	90	□ □
1591	**1028**	39p multicoloured	..	1·00	1·10	□ □
	Set of 5	..	3·25	3·50	□ □
	First Day Cover	..		4·50	□
	Presentation Pack ..	..	4·25		□
	PHQ Cards (set of 5) ..	..	3·00	6·50	□ □
	Set of 5 Gutter Pairs ..	..	6·50		□

1029 Flower Spray

1030 Double Locket

1031 Key

1032 Model Car and Cigarette Cards

1033 Compass and Map

1034 Pocket Watch

1035 1854 1d. Red Stamp and Pen

1036 Pearl Necklace

1037 Marbles

1038 Bucket, Spade and Starfish

T **1029/38** were printed together, se-tenant, in booklet panes of 10 stamps and 12 half stamp-size labels, the backgrounds of the stamps forming a composite design.

Greetings Stamps. "Memories".

1992 (28 Jan.) Two phosphor bands

1592	**1029**	(1st) multicoloured	..	40	45	□ □
	a. Booklet pane. Nos.					
	1592/1601		3·50		□
1593	**1030**	(1st) multicoloured	..	40	45	□ □
1594	**1031**	(1st) multicoloured	..	40	45	□ □
1595	**1032**	(1st) multicoloured	..	40	45	□ □
1596	**1033**	(1st) multicoloured	..	40	45	□ □
1597	**1034**	(1st) multicoloured	..	40	45	□ □
1598	**1035**	(1st) multicoloured	..	40	45	□ □
1599	**1036**	(1st) multicoloured	..	40	45	□ □
1600	**1037**	(1st) multicoloured	..	40	45	□ □
1601	**1038**	(1st) multicoloured	..	40	45	□ □
	Set of 10		3·50	4·00	□ □
	Presentation Pack		4·00		□
	First Day Cover			7·50	□

1039 Queen Elizabeth in Coronation Robes and Parliamentary Emblem

1040 Queen Elizabeth in Garter Robes and Archiepiscopal Arms

1046 Tennyson in 1856 and "April Love" (Arthur Hughes)

1047 Tennyson as a Young Man and "Mariana" (Dante Gabriel Rossetti)

1041 Queen Elizabeth with Baby Prince Andrew and Royal Arms

1042 Queen Elizabeth at Trooping the Colour and Service Emblems

1043 Queen Elizabeth and Commonwealth Emblem

Death Centenary of Alfred, Lord Tennyson (poet)

1992 (10 Mar.) *Phosphorised paper. Perf* $14\frac{1}{2} \times 14$.

1607	**1044**	24p multicoloured	..	50	50	☐ ☐
1608	**1045**	28p multicoloured	..	65	65	☐ ☐
1609	**1046**	33p multicoloured	..	1·10	1·10	☐ ☐
1610	**1047**	39p multicoloured	..	1·10	1·10	☐ ☐
		Set of 4	.. .. ..	3·00	3·00	☐ ☐
		First Day Cover ..	..		4·00	☐
		Presentation Pack	..	3·75		☐
		PHQ Cards (set of 4) ..	..	2·50	5·00	☐ ☐
		Set of 4 Gutter Pairs	..	6·00		☐

CARRICKFERGUS CASTLE   £1

1048 Carrickfergus Castle

1992 (24 Mar.) *Designs as Nos. 1410/13, but showing Queen's head in silhouette as T* **1048.** *Perf.* 15 × 14 (*with one elliptical hole on each vertical side*)

1611	**1048**	£1 bottle green and gold†	.. .. ..	1·50	1·50	☐ ☐
1612	**882**	£1·50 maroon and gold†	.. ..	2·25	2·25	☐ ☐
1613	**883**	£2 indigo and gold† ..	..	3·00	3·00	☐ ☐
1614	**884**	£5 deep brown and gold†	.. ..	7·50	7·50	☐ ☐
		Set of 4 ..	.. ..	13·00	13·00	☐ ☐
		First Day Cover ..	..		30·00	☐
		Presentation Pack	.. ..	14·50		☐
		PHQ Cards (set of 4)	.. ..	1·40		☐
		Set of 4 Gutter Pairs	..	27·00		☐

†The Queen's head on these stamps is printed in optically variable ink which changes colour from gold to green when viewed from different angles.

PHQ cards for Nos. 1611/14 were not issued until 2 March 1993.

Nos. 1602/6 were printed together, *se-tenant*, in horizontal strips of 5 throughout the sheet, forming a composite design.

40th Anniversary of Accession

1992 (6 Feb.) *Two phosphor bands. Perf* $14\frac{1}{2} \times 14$.

1602	**1039**	24p multicoloured	..	90	75	☐ ☐
		a. Horiz strip of 5.				
		Nos. 1602/6	..	4·00	3·50	☐ ☐
1603	**1040**	24p multicoloured	..	90	75	☐ ☐
1604	**1041**	24p multicoloured	..	90	75	☐ ☐
1605	**1042**	24p multicoloured	..	90	75	☐ ☐
1606	**1043**	24p multicoloured	..	90	75	☐ ☐
		Set of 5		4·00	3·50	☐ ☐
		First Day Cover ..	..		5·00	☐
		Presentation Pack	..	4·25		☐
		PHQ Cards (set of 5) ..	..	3·00	5·00	☐ ☐
		Gutter strip of 10	..	8·00		☐

1044 Tennyson in 1888 and "The Beguiling of Merlin" (Sir Edward Burne-Jones)

1045 Tennyson in 1864 and "I am Sick of the Shadows" (John Waterhouse)

1049 British Olympic Association Logo (Olympic Games, Barcelona)

1050 British Paralympic Association Symbol (Paralympics '92, Barcelona)

1051 *Santa Maria* (500th Anniv of Discovery of America by Columbus)

1052 *Kaisei* (Japanese cadet brigantine) (Grand Regatta Columbus, 1992)

1053 British Pavilion, "EXPO '92", Seville

Nos. 1615/16 were printed together, *se-tenant*, in horizontal pairs throughout the sheet.

Europa. International Events

1992 (7 APR.) *Phosphorised paper. Perf* $14 \times 14\frac{1}{2}$

1615	**1049**	24p multicoloured	..	65	65	☐ ☐
		a. Horiz pair.				
		Nos. 1615/16	..	1·25	1·25	☐ ☐
1616	**1050**	24p multicoloured	..	65	65	☐ ☐
1617	**1051**	24p multicoloured	..	65	65	☐ ☐
1618	**1052**	39p multicoloured	..	1·10	1·10	☐ ☐
1619	**1053**	39p multicoloured	..	1·10	1·10	☐ ☐
		Set of 5	..	3·75	3·75	☐ ☐
		First Day Cover	..		4·50	☐
		Presentation Pack ..	..	4·25		☐
		PHQ Cards (set of 5) ..	..	3·00	6·00	☐ ☐
		Set of 4 Gutter Pairs ..	..	7·50		☐

1054 Pikeman

1055 Drummer

1056 Musketeer

1057 Standard Bearer

350th Anniversary of the Civil War

1992 (16 JUNE) *Phosphorised paper. Perf* $14\frac{1}{2} \times 14$

1620	**1054**	24p multicoloured	..	55	55	☐ ☐
1621	**1055**	28p multicoloured	..	70	70	☐ ☐
1622	**1056**	33p multicoloured	..	1·00	1·00	☐ ☐
1623	**1057**	39p multicoloured	..	1·10	1·10	☐ ☐
		Set of 4	..	3·00	3·00	☐ ☐
		First Day Cover	..		4·00	☐
		Presentation Pack ..	..	3·75		☐
		PHQ Cards (set of 4) ..	..	2·00	5·00	☐ ☐
		Set of 4 Gutter Pairs ..	..	6·00		☐

1058 The Yeomen of the Guard

1059 The Gondoliers

1060 The Mikado

1061 The Pirates of Penzance